THE OFFICIAL
HEART OF MIDLOTHIAN
QUIZ BOOK

THE OFFICIAL HEART OF MIDLOTHIAN QUIZ BOOK

Compiled by Chris Cowlin
and Andrew-Henry Bowie

Foreword by Gary Mackay

APEX PUBLISHING LTD

First published in hardback in 2009 by
Apex Publishing Ltd
PO Box 7086, Clacton on Sea, Essex, CO15 5WN, England
www.apexpublishing.co.uk

British Library Cataloguing-in-Publication Data
A catalogue record for this book
is available from the British Library

ISBN: 1-906358-61-3   978-1-906358-61-7

Typeset in 10.5pt Chianti Bdlt Win95BT

Cover Design: Siobhan Smith

Printed and bound in Great Britain by the
MPG Books Group, Bodmin and King's Lynn

Author's Note:
Please contact me: **ChrisCowlin@btconnect.com** if you find any mistakes/errors in this book as I would like to put them right on any future reprints of this book. I would also like to hear from Hearts fans who have enjoyed the test! For more information on me and my books please look at: **www.ChrisCowlin.com**

This book is an official product of Heart of Midlothian Football Club.

FOREWORD
By Gary Mackay

It was a great pleasure to be asked to provide the foreword for this, The Official Heart of Midlothian Quiz Book. I've been a supporter of this wonderful team for over 40 years now, and for seventeen of them, I was privileged enough as a player, to make more appearances for the club than any other person. As both a supporter and as a player, those four decades have brought a multitude of highs and lows. The 70s led to a massive decline in fortunes, as the club was relegated and promoted almost year in/year out for seven years before the greatly respected era of the 80s under Alex MacDonald. Hearts have also played regularly and performed well in Europe. We've dominated the Edinburgh derby and of course won two Scottish Cups; both of which sparked off massive street celebrations in Gorgie. However, as well as all the great victories throughout those times, there have also been a whole host of painful defeats to endure; and often it's events off the pitch that are as much debated as the football played on it. Hearts are a big talking point, simply because the club means so much to so many people, and even those who don't support us still like to methodically study what's going on at Tynecastle! Heart of Midlothian is an institution steeped in history and drama, and this quiz book is the perfect vehicle for those Hearts' debates and conversations to keep going.

As supporters we all cherish the club and we want its future to be both stable and prosperous. Nevertheless, it's the past that gives our present day predicaments something to be compared with. This book is all about recollecting the past; those great games, the great goals and the great players. Hearts have had an eventful past to say the least, and I hope you enjoy remembering it as you make your way through a thousand quiz questions on the greatest and most successful football team Edinburgh has ever produced.

Enjoy the book!
Gary Mackay

INTRODUCTION
By Chris Cowlin

I would first of all like to thank Gary Mackay for writing the foreword to this book. I am very grateful for his help on this project and was truly delighted when he agreed to write a few words. I would also like to thank everyone for their comments and reviews (which can be found at the back of the book).

I would also like to thank Stephen McMenemy and Yifan Wu at Hearts for their help and advice during the book's compilation.

I have thoroughly enjoyed working on this book and researching the history of the club and its players.

It was great working with Andrew-Henry Bowie for the first time. I really hope you enjoy this book. Hopefully it should bring back some wonderful memories of this fantastic club!

In closing, I would like to thank all my friends and family for encouraging me to complete this project.

Best wishes
Chris Cowlin

INTRODUCTION
By Andrew-Henry Bowie

Heart of Midlothian FC: is there a finer name for a football team anywhere in the world? There is something quite magical about this old Edinburgh institution, yet its story is anything but a fairytale. The club's heritage is magnificent. The beautiful capital city of Edinburgh, the Royal Mile and the Heart of Midlothian cobble stones; our 1874 birth, the dark maroon jersey, the romantic heart-shaped crest, a glorious past and of course – that wonderful name. There are only a dozen professional football clubs in the world that can allege to be older in existence than Heart of Midlothian, yet few can claim to have such a vibrant, tumultuous and often tragic history. As a Hearts supporter, I've followed the club since the days when even getting out of Scottish football's second tier was proving to be too much of an ask, and yet I was one of the lucky ones! If every silver lining has a cloud, then it's those fantastic moments that sporadically come along that puts every defeat into context (and I'm gleefully writing this bit the day after we soundly beat Hibs on their own patch in the Scottish Cup). In my time as a supporter, there's been relegation; an agonising Championship loss and whole load of snatching defeats from the jaws of victory. Add to that a generation of heroes, two Scottish Cup wins and a multitude of great games and glorious goals to savour. This book is, on the whole, a reminder of the good times and great times; and may we live in interesting times. My vision when compiling this book was to one day take it round to my brother, Bobby's house and have a Hearts-themed 'pub quiz' with some friends. No doubt when it happens, I'll be on the receiving end of a torrent of verbal abuse as my keen knowledge of Heart of Midlothian puts his to diabolical shame. What would be even better than that is the Hearts family up and down the country, and beyond doing much the same thing with their own nearest and dearest. After all that we've been through; I think we deserve to take some time out to remind ourselves why it really is all worth it in the end. I sincerely hope you enjoy it. I'd like to dedicate this book to my wife, Lesley and to my daughter, Jude and to all the supporters, dreamers and believers of the famous Heart of Midlothian Football Club.

Best wishes
Andrew-Henry Bowie

Visit Chris Cowlin's website:

www.ChrisCowlin.com

Visit Andrew-Henry Bowie's website:

www.AndrewHenryBowie.co.uk

CLUB HISTORY

1. In what year was Heart of Midlothian FC formed?

2. On what famous public park by Melville Drive did Hearts play their early games?

3. Who was the first ever captain of Hearts?

4. Hearts were founding members of the Scottish League - in which year?

5. Who are Hearts' traditional city rivals?

6. What are the two traditional club colours of Hearts?

7. Up until May 2009, how many major domestic honours have Hearts won in their history?

8. What 'Park' or 'Stadium' have Hearts called home since 1886?

9. What event between 1914 and 1918 took greater precedence than football for the heroic Hearts players?

10. What is the popular rhyming nickname of 'Hearts'?

MANAGERS OF HEARTS

11. Who was manager of Hearts at the time of the Great War, 1914-18?

12. Who was manager of Hearts between Joe Jordan and Tommy McLean?

13. Who was manager of Hearts when the club suffered relegation in season 1980/81?

14. True or false: Tommy McLean was manager of Hearts in season 1995/96?

15. In which country was Csaba Laszlo born?

16. Who was joint manager of Hearts with Alex MacDonald from 1986 to 1988?

17. Billy Brown was assistant manager to whom?

18. Which former Hibernian legend was manager of Hearts between 1977 and 1980?

19. Who was manager of Hearts between 1941 and 1951?

20. Who was manager of Hearts between Craig Levein and George Burley?

GARY MACKAY - 'MR HEARTS'

21. In which year was Gary born – 1960, 1962 or 1964?

22. What high school did Gary attend?

23. In what year did Gary make his debut for Hearts?

24. In what year did Gary make his final appearance for Hearts?

25. How tall is Gary?

26. Against which country did Gary score on his Scotland debut?

27. Following on from the previous question, as a direct result of this goal which country qualified for the 1998 European Championships?

28. Against which team did Gary once score four goals in a Scottish Cup tie during January 1985 in a 6-0 win?

29. Which team did Gary join when his distinguished Hearts career ended?

30. True or false: with 640 competitive games, Gary is the all-time record appearance holder for Hearts?

WHERE DID THEY GO? – 1

*Match up the player with the club he
joined on leaving Hearts*

31.	Willie Jamieson	Morton
32.	Stephen Simmons	Celtic
33.	Roman Bednář	Livingston
34.	Jeremy Goss	Ayr United
35.	Iain Jardine	Dunfermline Athletic
36.	Darren Jackson	Dundee United
37.	Jim Townsend	Wigan Athletic
38.	Andy Webster	Colchester United
39.	Alan Gordon	Partick Thistle
40.	Tosh McKinlay	West Bromwich Albion

GREAT GAMES

41. Who scored the final goal of the game in Hearts' 5-3 win over Kilmarnock in 1997?

42. What was the score in the 88th minute of the 4-4 draw with Hibernian on 2 January 2003?

43. Name the four Hearts goalscorers in the 4-2 win over Rangers in September 2007.

44. Alan Gordon scored a hat-trick in a 6-3 win over which club in December 1964?

45. Who scored a double for the Jam Tarts in the 5-6 win over Dundee United in 1968?

46. Who scored all of Hearts' goals in a 5-5 League Cup draw with St Mirren in 1951?

47. What was the score between Hearts and Dundee on 11 November 1989?

48. Who scored a vital double for Hearts in a relegation battle at Tannadice on 6 April 1999?

49. At which stadium did the Maroons secure a 4-4 draw to win the 1959/60 Championship?

50. Which two Hearts players scored on their competitive debuts versus Kilmarnock in July 2005?

WHERE DID THEY GO? – 2

Match up the player with the club he joined on leaving Hearts

51.	Ian Baird	Falkirk
52.	Roy Barry	Walsall
53.	Dennis Wyness	Bristol City
54.	Gary Locke	Coventry City
55.	Neil Berry	Sunderland
56.	David Bowman	Dunfermline Athletic
57.	Fitzroy Simpson	Gala Fairydean
58.	Bobby Kirk	Dundee
59.	Derek Ferguson	Inverness Caledonian Thistle
60.	Cammy Fraser	Bradford City

CRAIG GORDON

61. Craig Gordon was born on Hogmanay of what year?

62. What high school did Craig attend?

63. Hearts loaned Craig out to which team in 2001?

64. Against which team did Craig make his competitive debut during October 2002 in a 1-1 draw?

65. Craig earned plaudits for his European debut performance against which team during November 2003 in a 1-0 win?

66. On 27 August 2005 Craig made an astonishing last-minute save from which Motherwell player?

67. Whose penalty did Craig save in the 2006 Scottish Cup final penalty shoot-out, with Hearts winning 4-2 on penalties after a 1-1 draw?

68. Whose British record transfer fee for a goalkeeper did Craig eclipse on joining Sunderland in 2007?

69. In 2007 which Italian international goalkeeper tipped Craig to become one of the best in the world?

70. Against which country did Craig make his international debut during May 2004 in a 4-1 win?

HEARTS IN THE SPL

71. Who scored Hearts' first ever SPL goal in the opening game of 1998/99 in a 2-1 win over Rangers?

72. In what League position did Hearts finish in the first SPL season, 1998/99?

73. Why were there no Edinburgh Derby games during season 1998/99?

74. Name the Serb, the Finn, the Jamaican and the Slovak that Jim Jefferies signed towards the end of 1999?

75. Which young striker scored Hearts' first goal of the 21st century, during a 2-0 win against Dundee during January 2000?

76. Which Ulsterman scored 13 goals for the Jam Tarts in season 2000/01?

77. True or false: Hearts' home jersey was v-necked in 2000/01 and round-necked in 2001/02?

78. Which two teams defeated Hearts in all four League meetings during season 2001/02?

79. Which Frenchman was ever-present during the 2002/03 League campaign?

80. Which Irishman scored an injury-time screamer to beat Partick Thistle on 14 December 2002 in a 1-0 win?

WHERE DID THEY COME FROM - 1?

Match up the player with the club he left to join Hearts

81.	Gordon Durie	Portsmouth
82.	Stéphane Mahé	Dundee
83.	Graeme Hogg	Rangers
84.	Ian Crawford	Gillingham
85.	Steven Boyack	Alloa Athletic
86.	Neil Pointon	Phoenix Inferno
87.	Frank Liddell	Celtic
88.	Eddie Thomson	Hamilton Academical
89.	Steve Banks	Oldham Athletic
90.	Peter Marinello	Penicuik Athletic

TOP LEAGUE GOALSCORERS

91. Who scored 44 League goals for the Maroons in season 1930/31?

92. Was it Andy Black or Tommy Walker who scored 31 League goals for Hearts in season 1936/37?

93. Which member of the Terrible Trio was Hearts' top League goalscorer for season 1955/56?

94. Who was Hearts' top League goalscorer for season 1964/65?

95. True or false: Drew Busby was Hearts' top League goalscorer for season 1973/74?

96. True or false: Donald Ford was Hearts' top League goalscorer for season 1974/75?

97. Which was John Robertson's most prolific goalscoring League campaign – 1985/86, 1987/88 or 1991/92?

98. Who was Hearts' top League goalscorer for season 1997/98?

99. Which Scotland striker was Hearts' top League goalscorer for season 1999/2000?

100. In which two seasons was Mark de Vries Hearts' top League goalscorer?

DREW BUSBY – THE BUZZ BOMB

101. In what year was Drew born?

102. True or false: Drew was born in Bathgate, West Lothian?

103. What was significant about Drew's last goal for Third Lanark FC in 1967?

104. From which club did Hearts sign Drew?

105. In what year did Drew sign for Hearts?

106. What transfer fee did Hearts pay for Drew?

107. Drew made his debut in a friendly against which Dutch team during August 1973 in a 1-0 win?

108. How many games did Drew play for Hearts - 194, 211 or 256?

109. How many goals did The Buzz Bomb score for Hearts in competitive games - 72, 84 or 98?

110. In what year did the curtain come down on Drew's fine Hearts career?

TYNECASTLE STADIUM

111. In what year did Hearts move to the current site of Tynecastle Stadium?

112. What was the final cost of the Main Stand on its completion in 1914 - £2,000, £6,000 or £12,000?

113. What is Tynecastle's all-time record attendance - 45,799, 49,131 or 53,396?

114. In which year was fencing and segregation introduced to Tynecastle - 1972, 1978 or 1982?

115. Which future World Player of the Year played in an Under-16s World Cup semi-final at Tynecastle on 20 June 1989?

116. The covered corner area of terracing that Hearts fans stood under between 1959 and 1994 was affectionately known as what?

117. What was the popular name of the terracing on which the Roseburn Stand now sits?

118. What name was given to the new stand that was built in 1994?

119. What is the name of the club that allowed fans to contribute financially towards the cost of the above new stand?

120. Submitted for planning in 2008, what is the proposed capacity for the new Main Stand?

HEARTS IN THE EUROPEAN CUP

121. What was the rather unfortunate scoreline from Hearts' first ever European Cup match during September 1958?

122. Following on from the previous question, who scored for the Jam Tarts in this game?

123. Following on again, what was the score in the return leg at Tynecastle during September 1958?

124. Which team went on to win the European Cup having knocked Hearts out in an earlier round?

125. Who scored Hearts' only goal of their two-legged European Cup tie in 1960?

126. True or false: legendary Portuguese striker Eusébio scored against Hearts in the European Cup in 1960?

127. Name the Bosnian team that Hearts played in a Champions League qualifier in 2006.

128. As well as an own goal, who were Hearts' scorers against the Bosnians at Murrayfield in a 3-0 win?

129. Who scored Hearts' goal against AEK Athens in a Champions League qualifier at Murrayfield in 2006?

130. True or false: following on from the previous question, teenage striker Calum Elliot started the match up front for Hearts in the return leg in Athens?

HAT-TRICK HEROES

131. Whose 'goal-den' vision bagged a hat-trick against Hibs on 1 January 1960 in a 5-1 win?

132. Whose hat-trick helped Hearts crush St Mirren 6-0 in February 1988 - John Colquhoun, John Robertson or Wayne Foster?

133. John Robertson scored a hat-trick against which outfit in January 1992?

134. Which Hearts player scored a Scottish Cup hat-trick against Stranraer in 2006/07 in a 4-0 win?

135. Which one of Paul Hartley's three goals against Hibs in the 2006 Scottish Cup semi-final was from open play in a 4-0 win?

136. Who scored an incredible hat-trick of four goals in three consecutive games for the Maroons in February 1926?

137. Who scored a hat-trick in the wonderful 5-3 win over Kilmarnock in 1997/98?

138. Whose hat-trick eased Hearts past Alloa in a September 2006 League Cup tie in a 4-0 win?

139. Who scored two hat-tricks against Aberdeen in 1999, one during a 5-2 win during May and the other during a 3-0 win in August?

140. Who scored a hat-trick against Airdrie during a Texaco Cup quarter-final tie during October 1970 in a 5-0 win?

MISCELLANEOUS - 1

141. What did Ian Baird do in 1993 that Scott Severin did in 2003 and that Lee Wallace also did in 2007?

142. Can you name two other professional football clubs formed in 1874?

143. Which former England international was a guest for Hearts in the Alex MacDonald Testimonial match?

144. Legendary Coronation Street barmaid Bet Lynch was alleged to have begun an unlikely public romance with which Hearts striker in 1994?

145. Which former Manchester United captain made his only appearance at Tynecastle on 30 April 2006?

146. Which Hearts player did Craig Gordon accidentally knock unconscious in the 2006 Scottish Cup semi-final in a 4-0 win?

147. Which former 1990s Hearts fullback went on to manage Watford in 2005?

148. True or false: up until season 2008/09 Hearts have never played an English team in European competition?

149. Which Swedish international did Hearts come close to signing in September 1997?

150. Which team did the Jam Tarts defeat 3-1 in an 'Unofficial World Champion' tie in 1902?

LATE, LATE GOALS

151. True or false: David Hagan smashed home a late equalising long-range shot into the top corner against Celtic on 25 February 1995 in a 1-1 draw?

152. Who set up two late goals for McKenna and Stamp to snatch victory at Easter Road in November 2002 in a 2-1 win against Hibernian?

153. Who, on scoring an injury-time goal at Easter Road, philosophically declared that "the game isn't over until the Fat Striker scores"?

154. Whose miraculous injury-time double denied Hibs victory, drawing 4-4 during January 2003?

155. In February 1984 John Robertson's injury-time overhead kick earned a 2-2 draw against which team - Paris St Germain, Celtic or Rangers?

156. Who scored an injury-time winner in the 2-1 win against Motherwell on 4 March 2009?

157. Which fullback's last-gasp screamer in the 2-1 win on 19 April 2003 caused severe damage to Celtic's title hopes?

158. Whose injury-time goal against Celtic in a 1-1 draw during 1998 provoked Jim Jefferies to run across the pitch in celebration?

159. In March 1986 which Hearts player poked home a late goal against Rangers while wearing only one boot in a 3-1 win?

160. Whose last-gasp penalty in a 1-1 draw during November 2005 rescued a point at Motherwell?

BOBBY WALKER – 'THE GREATEST EVER'

161. True or false: Bobby was older than the club?

162. Where was Bobby born - Glasgow, Belfast or Edinburgh?

163. True or false: the young Walker played a part in the 1896/97 League Championship triumph?

164. The 1901 Scottish Cup final in which Bobby played a key part is universally known as what?

165. Following on from the previous question, what was the score in the final with Bobby scoring one of the goals in the game?

166. As well as 1901, in which other year did Bobby win a Scottish Cup winners' medal?

167. How many League goals did Bobby score for Hearts - 121, 131 or 141?

168. In what year did Bobby retire as a player?

169. What role did Bobby go on to have at Hearts?

170. Which reigning monarch attended a Hearts match in 1912, specifically to see Bobby play?

BIG WINS

171. What was score in the 11-goal thriller against Hibs in season 1935/36?

172. Which player didn't score twice in the 7-1 trouncing of Dunfermline in 2001 – Róbert Tomaschek, Stéphane Adam or Andy Kirk?

173. True or false: the seven goals that Hearts scored against Hamilton in December 1986 were all by different players?

174. Hearts kicked off their ill-fated 1964/65 season with an 8-1 win against which Lanarkshire club?

175. Who scored his first two goals for Hearts in a 5-0 win against Falkirk on Boxing Day 2005?

176. Which two players each scored a hat-trick when Hearts won 7-0 at Arbroath on 24 December 1977?

177. Hearts eased past which Highland League team in the Cup on 9 January 1993 with a 6-0 win?

178. Which team did Hearts beat 15-0 in a Scottish Cup tie in 1937 – Kings Park, Queens Park or Queen of the South?

179. In which season did Hearts win League matches by the following scorelines: 9-0, 9-1, 8-0, 7-2 and 6-0?

180. What was score in the Edinburgh Derby game played on 12 August 1893?

HEARTS IN THE 1960s

181. Who scored Hearts' first goal of the 1960s in a 5-1 trouncing of Hibernian?

182. True or false: Hearts finished 4th in the League at the end of season 1959/60.

183. Hearts lost out on the 1964/65 League Championship by what margin of goal average?

184. Which team defeated Hearts in the 1960/61 League Cup final after a replay?

185. Which team defeated the Maroons in the 1968 Scottish Cup final?

186. Which team did Hearts play in Europe over two legs in November 1961?

187. Where did Hearts finish in the League at the end of season 1967/68?

188. Which Swiss team knocked Hearts out of Europe in season 1963/64?

189. Which 'Ernie' made his competitive debut for Hearts on 19 April 1969 in a 2-1 win against St Mirren?

190. Who scored Hearts' last goal of the 1960s in a 2-2 draw against Dundee United - Donald Ford, Roald Jensen, or Jim Townsend?

INTERNATIONAL CAPS

How many international caps did the following players win?

191. **Jimmy Murray**

192. **David Holt**

193. **Steven Pressley**

194. **Charlie Thomson**

195. **Andy Anderson**

196. **Barney Battles**

197. **Craig Levein**

198. **Jimmy Wardhaugh**

199. **Alfie Conn**

200. **Gary Mackay**

2003/2004

201. Which three players scored their first goals for Hearts in season 2003/04?

202. Which Australian international made his Hearts debut during August 2003 in a 1-0 win against Dunfermline Athletic?

203. Which youngster made his debut for Hearts at Tannadice on 30 November 2003 in a 2-1 defeat against Dundee United - Craig Gordon, Robert Sloan or Christophe Berra?

204. Who played the most competitive games for Hearts in season 2003/04?

205. Who was the Jam Tarts' top goalscorer in season 2003/04 with 15 goals?

206. What was unusual about both of Hearts' goals in the Edinburgh Derby on 23 November 2003?

207. Who put Hearts into the lead against Rangers at Ibrox on 20 December 2003 in a 2-1 defeat?

208. Who scored Hearts' winner in a 1-0 win against Rangers at Ibrox on 12 May 2004?

209. What was Hearts' final League position in season 2003/04?

210. What was significant about Hearts' points tally of 68 this season?

HOW MUCH DID THEY COST?

Match up the player with the transfer fee paid by Hearts

211.	Mike Galloway	£300,000
212.	Ian Baird	£300,000
213.	Jim Weir	£30,000
214.	Michal Pospíšil	£60,000
215.	Kevin McKenna	£350,000
216.	Derek Ferguson	£850,000
217.	Kenny Black	£100,000
218.	Alan Maybury	£300,000
219.	Willie Pettigrew	£750,000
220.	Mirsad Bešlija	£120,000

THE TERRIBLE TRIO

221. Which three legends made up The Terrible Trio?

222. Which member of The Terrible Trio was born in
      England?

223. What was the score in the first competitive match that
      The Terrible Trio played in together, during October
      1948?

224. Which member of The Terrible Trio scored the most
      competitive goals for Hearts?

225. Which two members of The Terrible Trio were joint-top
      scorers for season 1950/51, both scoring 24 goals?

226. How many goals did The Terrible Trio score against
      Hibs in a Scottish Cup tie played on 5 February 1955 in
      a 5-0 win?

227. Which member of The Terrible Trio failed to score
      against Hibs in a 6-1 League victory in 1956?

228. How many of The Terrible Trio scored in the 5-1
      League victory over Hibs on 1 January 1955?

229. Which member of The Terrible Trio was sometimes
      referred to as 'Twinkletoes'?

230. Which member of The Terrible Trio was known simply
      as 'The King of Hearts'?

PLAYERS' NATIONALITIES – 1

Match up the player with his nationality

231.	Christian Nadé	Danish
232.	Peter Van de Ven	Angolan
233.	Nerijus Barasa	Ugandan
234.	Colin Miller	Scottish
235.	David Obua	Canadian
236.	Alex Massie	English
237.	José Quitongo	Dutch
238.	René Moller	Portuguese
239.	Darren Beckford	French
240.	Bruno Aguiar	Lithuanian

CLASSIC MATCH 1976 –
HEARTS 5, LOCOMOTIV LEIPZIG 1

241. In which tournament were Hearts and Locomotiv competing?

242. What was the score in the first leg in Leipzig?

243. Who scored a double for Hearts in the return leg at Tynecastle?

244. Following on from the previous question, who scored the other three goals for the Maroons?

245. Following on again, who played in goal for Hearts in this match?

246. Who was the Hearts manager at the time?

247. Where did Jim Jefferies start the match?

248. Who was Hearts' youngest player on the pitch, aged 21?

249. How many Scots played a part in the game for Hearts?

250. Which team did Hearts meet in the next round of the competition?

PLAYERS' NATIONALITIES – 2

Match up the player with his nationality

251.	Samuel Camazzola	Greek
252.	Tepi Moilanen	Czech
253.	Mauricio Pinilla	Spanish
254.	Anthony Basso	Chilean
255.	Roman Bednář	Icelandic
256.	Juanjo	Brazilian
257.	Takis Fyssas	Finnish
258.	Jamie Mole	Scottish
259.	Basil Colombo	French
260.	Eggert Jónsson	English

HEART-BREAKING MOMENTS

261. Which team defeated Hearts 2-0 in an agonising last day of the season title decider in 1964/65?

262. Who scored two goals for Dundee in a 2-0 defeat to deny Hearts the League title on 3 May 1986?

263. What was the name of the assistant referee who controversially flagged for a penalty in favour of Rangers in a 2-1 defeat during March 2005?

264. What was the name of the referee who deemed it necessary to send off four Hearts players at Ibrox in a 3-0 defeat on 14 September 1996?

265. In what lowly League position did Hearts finish the 1921/22 season?

266. Which team defeated Hearts 3-0 in the 1986 Scottish Cup final?

267. On what date did Hibernian register their biggest ever win over Hearts, a 7-0 defeat?

268. Which Hearts player scored an own goal three minutes into injury time against AEK Athens in a Champions League qualifier in 2006 in a 2-1 defeat?

269. Which player scored two second-half goals to deny the Jam Tarts victory in the 1996/97 Coca Cola Cup final in a 4-3 defeat against Rangers?

270. Which Hearts captain badly injured his knee ligaments just minutes into the 1996 Scottish Cup final, in a 5-1 defeat against Rangers?

PLAYER OF THE YEAR

271.   Who won the SPFA Young Player of the Year award for 1983/84?

272.   Which UEFA Champions League medallist was also a five-time winner of the Lithuanian Player of the Year award?

273.   Who was the Scottish Footballer of the Year for season 1985/86?

274.   Which former Hearts striker won the French Footballer of the Year award in 1989?

275.   Who won the SPFA Young Player of the Year award for both 1984/85 and 1985/86?

276.   Which former Hearts great won the English FWA Footballer of the Year award for season 1968/69?

277.   Which Irishman and former Hearts player won the PFAI Player of the Year award in 1984?

278.   Who won the club's own Young Player of the Year Award for 2008/09?

279.   Who won the Czech 'Revelation of the Season' award for 2004/05, shortly before his transfer to Hearts?

280.   True or false: Paul Hartley won the Scottish Footballer of the Year award for season 2005/06?

TOMMY WALKER OBE

281. In which West Lothian village was Tommy born?

282. In what year did Tommy sign for the Maroons?

283. Hearts rejected a potential world record transfer fee for Tommy from which London club in season 1934/35?

284. Why did it take so long for Tommy to score a vital penalty kick against England in a 1-1 draw at Wembley in 1936?

285. Tommy scored against England again at Wembley two years later. What was the final score?

286. True or false: Tommy scored just under 200 competitive goals for Hearts.

287. Tommy eventually starred for which London team?

288. For how many years was Tommy manager of Hearts?

289. How many major trophies did Hearts win under Tommy's management?

290. In what year did Tommy retire as a Hearts director?

HEARTS v. HIBS

291.   True or false: Hearts first played Hibs on Christmas Day.

292.   How many goals did Mark de Vries score the first time he faced Hibs, in the 5-1 win during Augsut 2002?

293.   Following on from the previous question, who won the 'Man of the Match' award that day?

294.   Who scored Hearts' late winner at Easter Road in a 2-1 win on 25 August 1984?

295.   How many competitive derby games did Hearts win in the 1970s?

296.   How many competitive derby games did Hearts lose in the 1980s?

297.   True or false: both teams overall have a stronger record against the other while playing at home.

298.   Which Pole became a cult hero among Hearts fans due to his erratic goalkeeping in 2005 and 2006?

299.   On what did Hans Eskilsson lay the blame for missing an open goal in the 1996 New Year derby?

300.   Which youngster scored the Maroons' killer second goal in the 2-0 win in the Scottish Cup derby in January 2009?

LEAGUE CHAMPIONS

301. Up until 2009, how many times have Hearts been Scottish League Champions?

302. In which seasons did Hearts become Scottish League Champions?

303. What did Hibernian FC win in the same season that Hearts first became Scottish League Champions?

304. Who finished second in the League behind Hearts in season 1896/97?

305. Hearts scored a staggering British top-flight record of how many goals in season 1957/58?

306. How many League games did the Jam Tarts lose in 1957/58?

307. By how many points did second place Rangers trail behind Hearts at the end of season 1957/58?

308. In how many competitive games did Hearts score six goals or more in season 1957/58?

309. True or false: Hearts scored more than 100 goals on their way to becoming Champions in season 1959/60.

310. Who finished second in the League behind Hearts in season 1959/60?

HEARTS v. RANGERS

311. Who scored a double for Hearts in a 3-0 win at Ibrox in November 1963 - Willie Wallace, Tommy White or Johnny Hamilton?

312. Whose hat-trick at Ibrox stunned Rangers in a 3-0 win during January 1996?

313. In December 1972 which player audaciously sat on the ball seconds before Hearts scored the only goal of the game at Ibrox?

314. How many times did Hearts beat Rangers during season 1985/86?

315. Whose 14th-minute header sent Tynecastle into raptures on 24 September 2005?

316. Who disguised himself as the club mascot, 'Hearty Harry', just a week before scoring two goals against Hearts in the Coca-Cola Cup final in a 4-3 defeat in 1996?

317. What was the score between the two teams when they met in the quarter-finals of the Scottish Cup in 1956?

318. Which ex-Rangers player scored for Hearts in a 3-1 win on 10 September 1983?

319. Whose own goal didn't stop Hearts from beating Rangers 2-1 on 22 November 2008?

320. On 16 November 1985 which former Rangers defender played in his 1000th career match?

HEARTS IN THE 1990s

321. Which two teams each defeated Hearts three times in the Scottish Cup in the 1990s?

322. Who was the first player to make his competitive debut for the Maroons in the 1990s in a 1-1 draw against Rangers during May 1990?

323. What was the score between Hearts and Hibs on 1 January 1990?

324. In which 1990s season did Hearts achieve a runners-up position?

325. Name all five Hearts managers in the 1990s.

326. Name all five kit manufacturers for Hearts in the 1990s.

327. Name the four non-Scots who debuted for Hearts in season 1995/96.

328. Name the four Hearts players sent off at Ibrox on 14 September 1996.

329. Name the Hearts starting line-up that defeated Rangers 2-1 in the 1997/98 Scottish Cup final.

330. What SPL League position did Hearts occupy at the beginning of April 1999?

HEARTS v. CELTIC

331.   Who scored a double to sink Celtic 2-1 in the first home game of season 2006/07?

332.   What was the score when the sides met in a Scottish Cup quarter-final tie on 5 March 1966?

333.   Which two Hearts players were sent off in a stormy Scottish Cup tie against Celtic on 18 March 1989 in a 2-1 defeat?

334.   John Robertson scored the only goal in a 1-0 win over Celtic on 12 October 1985, but it turned out to be a bitter-sweet day for him - why?

335.   Whose double saw off Celtic in a 2-1 win on 6 December 1998 - Jim Hamilton, Colin Cameron or Stéphane Adam?

336.   On 21 February 1987, 28,891 fans witnessed which Hearts player scoring the only goal of a Scottish Cup tie between the teams?

337.   True or false: Hearts faced Celtic in an Inter-Cities Fairs Cup tie in 1966.

338.   Who scored a hat-trick for the Jam Tarts in 3-4 defeat to Celtic on 20 November 1976?

339.   Whose long-range free kick stunned Celtic in a 1-1 draw on 11 April 2009?

340.   Which two players scored in quick succession in a 2-1 win at Celtic Park on 4 January 1992 to keep Hearts top of the League?

DONALD FORD

341. In which West Lothian town was Donald born - Whitburn, Linlithgow or Fauldhouse?

342. In what year did Tommy Walker sign Donald for the Maroons?

343. Donald was studying for what profession while starring for Hearts?

344. In all, how many competitive goals did Donald score for Hearts - 110, 129 or 143?

345. For how many seasons in a row was Donald Hearts' top scorer?

346. How many international caps did Donald win?

347. Donald represented his country in which other sport?

348. What team did Donald join on leaving Hearts in 1976?

349. True or false: Donald played for Scotland against Brazil in the 1974 World Cup.

350. Which new career did Donald begin in 1991?

HEARTS v. ABERDEEN

351. Whose last-minute goal sank Aberdeen 2-1 in the 1996 Scottish Cup semi-final?

352. Which player scored near identical goals against The Dons on consecutive weeks in February 2006?

353. What was the score in Sir Alex Ferguson's last game in charge of Aberdeen against Hearts on 13 September 1986?

354. How many goals did Hearts score in their ten-match unbeaten run against The Dons from 1956 to 1960 - 18, 22 or 35?

355. Hearts steamrollered Aberdeen 3-0 in a Scottish Cup tie in February 2006, but what was the half-time score?

356. Who scored for Hearts in a 1-0 League Cup win in November 2002?

357. In 2008 which Hearts player scored a winning goal against Aberdeen, only to be accused of being 'lazy' by losing boss, Jimmy Calderwood?

358. How many goals did Hearts score against Aberdeen in season 1997/98 - 9, 13 or 15?

359. Which Hearts player was sent off in the 1986 Scottish Cup final against Aberdeen?

360. Name two of the four Hearts scorers in the 4-1 win over Aberdeen on 11 November 2007.

SCOTTISH CUP WINNERS

361. Up until 2009, how many times have Hearts won the
      Scottish Football Association Challenge Cup?

362. In what year did the Maroons first win the Scottish
      Cup?

363. Which team have Hearts twice beaten in a Scottish Cup
      final?

364. What was unique about the staging of the 'Heart of
      Mid-Lothian v. Hibernians' Scottish Cup final of 1896?

365. What was the score in the Edinburgh Derby final of
      1896?

366. Who scored twice for Hearts in a 3-1 win in front of a
      massive 133,583 crowd in the 1956 Cup final win over
      Celtic?

367. Which iconic Frenchman scored the clincher for Hearts
      in the 2-1 1998 Cup win?

368. Name the Austrian, the Italian, the Greek and the
      Senegalese players who have won Scottish Cup
      winners' medals with Hearts.

369. Name the four unused Hearts substitutes in the Cup
      wins of 1998 and 2006.

370. Which Hearts player earned the new nickname 'The
      Tackle' after the 1-1 draw and then 4-2 penalty shoot-
      out win in the 2006 Cup win over Gretna?

HEARTS v. DUNDEE UNITED

371.   Who scored the winner for Hearts in the incredible
        6-5 Scottish Cup win in 1968 - René Moller, Jim Irvine
        or Donald Ford?

372.   Beginning in 1979 Dundee United enjoyed a 14-game
        unbeaten run against Hearts that finally ended in
        which year?

373.   True or false: Hearts had a 12-year 22-game unbeaten
        run against Dundee United at Tynecastle in the 1980s
        and 1990s.

374.   Whose exquisite volley separated the two sides in a
        1-0 win in the Scottish Cup semi-final in 1986?

375.   In the 1926 Scottish Cup what was the 2nd replay
        scoreline between the teams following two 1-1 draws?

376.   In which season did Hearts and Dundee United share
        four excruciating 0-0 draws?

377.   Who is Hearts' all-time top goalscorer in games against
        Dundee United, with 18 goals?

378.   True or false: no member of The Terrible Trio ever
        scored against Dundee United.

379.   Who scored the only goal of the game at Tannadice on
        28 February 2009, leaving his old boss unhappy?

380.   Who struck a quite sensational half-volley into the top
        corner of Dundee United's goal in a 3-0 win on 12
        April 1986?

2004/2005

381. How many players made their debuts for the Jam Tarts in season 2004/05 - 7, 10 or 13?

382. Name four of the eight players who scored their first goals for Hearts during January and February 2005.

383. Who played the most competitive games for Hearts in season 2004/05?

384. Who was Hearts' top goalscorer in season 2004/05 with 15 goals?

385. What opposition manager did Hearts come up against in a UEFA Cup match against Feyenoord in October 2004?

386. Who took temporary charge of Hearts for one League game against Dundee on 30 October 2004?

387. Who were the opposition in John Robertson's first game in charge of Hearts during November 2004?

388. Who scored for Hearts in a 2-0 win at Celtic Park in April 2005?

389. Who bought control of Hearts in early 2005, saving Tynecastle in the process?

390. Which Rangers defender was deemed to have been fouled by Lee Miller towards the end of the controversial 2-1 defeat on 2 March 2005?

LEAGUE POSITIONS – 1

*Match up the season with Hearts' finishing
position in the League*

391.	1983/84	2nd
392.	1896/97	11th
393.	2001/02	2nd
394.	1966/67	10th
395.	1959/60	5th
396.	1980/81	2nd
397.	1975/76	1st
398.	1956/57	5th
399.	2005/06	5th
400.	1991/92	1st

JOHN CUMMING – 'THE IRON MAN'

401. In which year was John born – 1930, 1933, or 1937?

402. Where was John born – Carluke, Motherwell, or Harthill?

403. Against which Old Firm team did John make his Hearts debut in a 2-2 draw during December 1950?

404. How many major honours did John win with the Maroons?

405. How many Hearts players have won as many or more honours with the club than John?

406. How many competitive games did John play for Hearts stretching over 16 years – 465, 505, or 525?

407. How many goals did John score for Hearts - 17, 31 or 44?

408. How many Scotland caps did John win?

409. In what year did John play the last game of his glittering Hearts career?

410. What did John do in the wake of suffering a severe head cut in the 1956 Scottish Cup final?

HEARTS – THE EARLY YEARS

411.   In what other pastime did the founding 'Heart of Mid-Lothian' players partake, whose premises inspired the name of their new football team?

412.   To what Southside ground did Hearts move in 1878/79 to escape the overcrowded Meadows?

413.   Which team thumped Hearts 7-1 in the 1886/87 FA Cup - Preston North End, Corinthians or Darwen?

414.   In 1882 which side inflicted an 8-1 defeat on Hearts, a record reverse that still stands to this day?

415.   What was the score when Hearts played Anchor in the EFA Shield on 30 October 1880?

416.   What tavern was registerd as Hearts' first ever headquarters – Anderson's, Dicken's or Robertson's?

417.   Hearts' first honour came in 1878 when they beat which team 3-2 in the 4th replay of the Edinburgh FA Cup?

418.   True or false: Hearts won the Scottish Cup four times between 1891 and 1906?

419.   In 1886 Hearts beat which side 4-1 in the first game at their new Tynecastle home – Chelsea, Queens Park Rangers or Bolton Wanderers?

420.   True or false: Percy Dawson's transfer from Hearts to Blackburn Rovers in 1914 was at that time the world's second highest transfer fee?

CLASSIC MATCH 1989 - HEARTS 1, BAYERN MUNICH 0

421. Who scored a screamer of a goal for Hearts in the 1-0 win over Bayern Munich?

422. At what 'End' of Tynecastle was the goal scored?

423. Seconds before The Shed erupted, who teed the goal up with a short free-kick pass to his left?

424. Name the only three Hearts players over the age of 25 who played that night?

425. Who was the youngest Hearts player that night at just 18 years old?

426. Name the only non-Scot to feature for the Jam Tarts that night?

427. What was the match attendance - 19,312, 20,016 or 26,294?

428. What was the unlucky second-leg score in Munich?

429. Which World Cup winning defender scored a spectacular goal for Bayern in the second leg?

430. Who went on to beat Bayern in the semi-finals and won the 1988/89 UEFA Cup?

LEAGUE POSITIONS – 2

Match up the season with Hearts' finishing position in the League

431.	1987/88	1st
432.	1997/98	4th
433.	1953/54	1st
434.	1914/15	3rd
435.	1994/95	2nd
436.	1969/70	9th
437.	1957/58	2nd
438.	1976/77	3rd
439.	1894/95	6th
440.	1999/2000	2nd

'THE YO-YO YEARS' - 1977-1983

441. How many times were Hearts relegated between seasons 1976/77 and 1982/83?

442. In which calendar years were Hearts relegated?

443. True or false: Hearts have never been relegated before or since that period?

444. In which season did Hearts fail to win promotion back to the Premier League?

445. Against which team did Hearts set a First Division attendance record of 19,399 at Tynecastle in a 2-2 draw during January 1978?

446. Who scored a late goal in a1-0 win against Airdrieonians to clinch the First Division title for the Maroons in 1980?

447. What was the score between Celtic and relegation-bound Hearts on April Fools' Day 1981?

448. Which team knocked Hearts out of the Scottish Cup, losing 1-0 on 13 February 1982?

449. Name the flamboyant Edinburgh businessman who gained control of Hearts in 1981.

450. Who became Hearts' first player/manager in 1982, as the club's revival began?

IN WHAT YEAR DID WE SIGN?

Match the player with the year he signed for Hearts

451.	David Weir	1971
452.	Alan Anderson	1996
453.	Johnny Hamilton	1984
454.	Robbie Neilson	1990
455.	Willie Gibson	1996
456.	Steven Pressley	1967
457.	Neil Berry	1963
458.	Stevie Fulton	1955
459.	Gary Locke	1988
460.	Jim Brown	1995

JIM CRUICKSHANK

461. Where was Jim born - Edinburgh, Glasgow or Toronto?

462. In what year did Jim make his Hearts debut?

463. In what year did Jim make his final appearance for the Jam Tarts?

464. Which West of Scotland club did Jim face in both his first and last games for Hearts?

465. With 528 games for Hearts, where does Jim rank in the all-time appearances list?

466. How tall is Jim?

467. From which club did Hearts sign Jim?

468. Against which country did Jim make his Scotland debut in 1964 in a 2-2 draw?

469. How many international caps did the outstanding Cruickshank win?

470. From which Hibernian player did Jim make a stunning 'triple penalty save' in January 1967?

GREAT GOALKEEPERS

471.   Which 'Wembley Wizard' kept goal for Hearts in the
        1920s and 1930s?

472.   Whose impressive displays in the 1980s forced Jimmy
        Greaves to re-evaluate publicly his opinion of Scottish
        goalkeepers?

473.   Who was in goal for Hearts' historic Scottish Cup
        victory in 1956?

474.   Jim Cruickshank played in the 1970 Scotland v.
        England home International match. What was the
        score?

475.   True or false: Gordon Marshall played fewer games for
        the Maroons than Kenny Garland?

476.   Jake Reid was given what nickname, which didn't
        prevent him from becoming Hearts' first goalkeeper?

477.   Which hugely talented goalkeeper denied Dunfermline
        victory with a magnificent penalty save during a 2-0
        win on 20 April 2002?

478.   Which sub goalkeeper was thrown into an Edinburgh
        derby in a 1-1 draw during October 2008?

479.   Which side did Craig Gordon thwart with a miraculous
        reactionary save during a 2-1 win in the Scottish Cup
        quarter-final match in February 2006?

480.   Who made a triple save to frustrate Celtic's van
        Hooijdonk, Di Canio and Cadete in Hearts' Coca Cola
        Cup quarter-final 1-0 victory in 1996?

HEARTS IN THE 1970s

481. Which 'Eric' was the first Hearts player of the 1970s to make his competitive debut for the club, in a 1-0 win against St Mirren?

482. Who won the Edinburgh derby at Easter Road on 1 January 1970?

483. Who scored Hearts' first goal of the 1970s, in a 2-0 win over Dunfermline Athletic - Andy Lynch, David Clunie or Neil Murray?

484. In which season did Hearts launch their dashing 'Ajax'-style home kit?

485. What was the score in the first Edinburgh derby of the 1973/74 season?

486. True or false: Hearts finished bottom of the first Premier League season, 1975/76?

487. What was unusual about Rangers' opening goal against Hearts in the 1976 Scottish Cup final?

488. Who scored Hearts' last goal of the 1970s - Bobby Masterton, Des O'Sullivan or Pat McShane?

489. In which 1970s season did Malcolm Robertson, Eamonn Bannon and Brian Wilson make their competitive Hearts debuts?

490. Who were the only two Hearts players to be capped for Scotland in the 1970s?

CLASSIC MATCH - SCOTTISH CUP FINAL 1998

491. Which Academy Award-winning Hollywood star was left stunned by the sheer size of Hearts' support when attending the final?

492. Who was fouled on the edge of the box in the first minute, winning the Jam Tarts a penalty?

493. Who changed his mind in the penalty run-up, sending his spot kick high into the net to make the score 1-0 to Hearts?

494. Who dispossessed Lorenzo Amoruso on 52 minutes to fire Hearts towards their first silverware in 36 years?

495. Whose audacious overhead flick left the Rangers defence bamboozled on 70 minutes?

496. Name the Hearts substitute who performed heroically after coming on in the 78th minute.

497. Who denied Sergio Porrini a chance with a last-gasp tackle late in the game - Stefano Salvatori, Neil McCann or David Weir?

498. Along with legendary striker John Robertson, name Hearts' other unused substitute on the day.

499. By what mode of transport did the victorious team travel to Tynecastle on the following day?

500. True or false: 1998 was the last year that the real Scottish Football Association Challenge Cup left Glasgow?

'H-E-A ...' - GREAT SONGS FROM THE TERRACES

501. In 'The Hearts Song', which four players can always be supplied with national caps?

502. 'Follow the Hearts, and you can't go ...'?

503. What festive classic was belted out 'in the snow' on 24 December 1977 by Hearts fans as their heroes destroyed Arbroath 7-0?

504. In the 'Europe Song', what infrastructure would Hearts fans be willing to dig just to see their beloved team play?

505. Where, according to the 'Europe Song', will Hibs be residing by the time 'we're overseas'?

506. Whose chickens sponsored the B-side to the 1986 released version of 'The Hearts Song'?

507. Which Englishman became 'Super' after scoring the winning goal in the Scottish Cup Edinburgh derby fourth- round tie in 1994?

508. Which 1970s legend 'bides at Tynecastle, just over the Forth'?

509. Into whose net did 'Johnny Robertson' invariably put the ball?

510. What Beatles classic is usually accompanied by a swarm of twirling maroon and white scarves?

CLASSIC MATCH 2006 - HIBS 0, HEARTS 4

511.   In which competition were the teams playing?

512.   Who scored a hat-trick for Hearts in the game?

513.   Following on from the previous question, can you name the Lithuanian forward who scored the other goal in the game after 81 minutes?

514.   Name the two Hibs players that were sent off during this match.

515.   At which stadium was the match played?

516.   Can you name Hibs' Polish goalkeeper?

517.   What was the score at half-time?

518.   Can you name the Scottish referee who was in charge of the match?

519.   What was the attendance for this match – 33,180, 38,180 or 43,180?

520.   Which Hearts manager guided the club to victory?

WILLIE BAULD – 'THE KING'

521.   In which year was Willie born – 1928, 1930 or 1932?

522.   Where was Willie born – Broomhall, Danderhall or Newcraighall?

523.   True or false: Willie is in the top ten in the all-time list of competitive appearances made by Hearts players?

524.   What was Willie's two middle names?

525.   In a total of 414 competitive games for Hearts, how many goals did Willie score - 249, 266 or 277?

526.   How many goals did Willie score in his first competitive game for Hearts during a 6-1 win over East Fife?

527.   How many goals did Willie score in his second competitive game for Hearts during a 5-0 win over Queen of the South?

528.   In total how many competitive hat-tricks did Willie score for Hearts?

529.   Despite being a prolific scorer for the Maroons, how many full Scotland caps did Willie win?

530.   True or false: all of Willie's full Scotland caps were won in the same year?

CLASSIC MATCH –
SCOTTISH CUP FINAL 2006

531.   Which team did Hearts beat in the final?

532.   What was the score after extra time?

533.   Which Jam Tarts player was sent off after 120 minutes?

534.   Which Czech Republic midfielder opened the scoring for Hearts after 39 minutes?

535.   At which stadium was the final played?

536.   Can you name one of the three Hearts substitutes used in the game?

537.   Who played in goal for Hearts during the final?

538.   Which team did Hearts beat in the quarter-finals, winning 2-1 at home during February 2006?

539.   What was the attendance in the final – 51,232, 53,232 or 55,232?

540.   By what score did Hearts beat the opposition on penalties after extra time?

HEARTS IN THE UEFA CUP

541. Name the three Prague-based teams that Hearts have faced in the UEFA Cup?

542. The competition was founded in 1971, but in what year did Hearts play their first UEFA Cup match?

543. Up until 2008/09, what has been Hearts biggest margin of victory over 90 minutes in the UEFA Cup?

544. Up until 2008/09, what has been Hearts biggest defeat in the UEFA Cup?

545. Which player has appeared in the UEFA Cup more times for Hearts than any other?

546. Name the four clubs that the Maroons faced in their exciting run to the quarter-finals in season 1988/89.

547. True or false: Hearts were the first British club to qualify for the inaugural UEFA Cup group stages?

548. Name the five teams that Hearts faced in their historic UEFA Cup campaign of season 2004/05.

549. Who is Hearts' all-time top goalscorer in the UEFA Cup?

550. Who was the match winner in Hearts' sensational 1-0 victory at Bordeaux in 2003?

CRAIG LEVEIN

551. What is Craig's middle name – Charles, William or Harold?

552. What award did Craig win while a Hearts player in 1985 and 1986?

553. In what year was Craig appointed manager of the Jam Tarts?

554. How many full international caps did Craig win for Scotland – 16, 20 or 24?

555. Apart from Hearts, can you name the other club that Craig played for and then managed?

556. How many League goals did Craig score during his Hearts career – 15, 20 or 25?

557. In what year did Craig join Hearts?

558. Following on from the previous question, which Jam Tarts manager signed Craig for Hearts?

559. How many League games did Craig play for Hearts in his football career - 326, 426 or 526?

560. In what position did Craig mostly play during his playing days?

'FORGOTTEN' PLAYERS

561. Which 'Robbie' made his first and only appearance for Hearts at Tannadice on 3 May 1997?

562. Which 31-year-old made his only appearance for Hearts as a substitute in a match against Slavia Prague in 1992?

563. Which young goalkeeper warmed the bench for Hearts at the 1996 Scottish Cup final?

564. Which Portuguese midfielder made his only League appearance for Hearts on 26 August 2006?

565. Which two players made their first and only competitive appearances in a 1-6 defeat at Motherwell in 2002?

566. Which 16-year-old made two League Cup appearances for the Jam Tarts in season 1983/84?

567. Which tough-tackling former Rangers midfielder made five on-loan appearances for Hearts between February and March 1984?

568. Which player made his only appearance for bottom-of-the-table Hearts at Dens Park on 20 March 1999?

569. Which Lithuanian player made eight on-loan appearances for Hearts in season 2004/05?

570. Which Frenchman played 22 games for Hearts and scored 3 goals in season 1996/97?

SANDY JARDINE

571.   In what position did Sandy play during his Hearts playing days?

572.   In what year did Sandy join Hearts as co-manager from Rangers?

573.   In which decade did Sandy manage the Jam Tarts?

574.   How many goals did Sandy score for Scotland in his 38 full international appearances?

575.   Following on from the previous question, in how many of his 38 appearances for Scotland did Sandy captain the team – 9, 19 or 29?

576.   How many League appearances did Sandy make for Hearts in his career –187, 207 or 227?

577.   'Sandy' is a nickname that was given to him in his younger days due to his sand-coloured hair. What is his real first name?

578.   True or false: Sandy once managed Rangers?

579.   How many League goals did Sandy score for Hearts in his career – 3, 4 or 5?

580.   In which year was Sandy born in Edinburgh – 1946, 1948 or 1950?

HENRY SMITH

581. In which Cup-winning year was Henry born?

582. True or false: Henry is Hearts' record appearance holder for a goalkeeper?

583. Including friendly matches, how many appearances did Henry make for Hearts – 500, 600 or 700?

584. In what year did Henry make his debut for Hearts?

585. From which Yorkshire club did the Jam Tarts sign Henry?

586. Henry denied which Dundee United left back a goal when he made an astonishing save on 12 April 1986?

587. Which Celtic striker did Henry thwart with a miraculous 'tip over the bar' save on 16 November 1991?

588. How many Scotland caps did Henry win?

589. In what year did Henry make his final appearance for Hearts?

590. True or false: Henry scored a penalty kick in his final match for Hearts?

'SUPER' WAYNE FOSTER

591.   In what position did Wayne play during his playing days?

592.   In which year was Wayne born in Tyldesley – 1961, 1962 or 1963?

593.   How many League goals did Wayne score in his first season at Tynecastle – 4, 6 or 8?

594.   Which manager handed Wayne his Hearts debut?

595.   Which team did Wayne join in 1994 when he left Tynecastle?

596.   How many League goals did Wayne score for Hearts during his playing career – 12, 22 or 32?

597.   Against which team did Wayne score the winning goal for Hearts in a 2-1 away win in the Scottish Cup during February 1994?

598.   How many League appearances did Wayne make for Hearts during his career – 160, 180 or 200?

599.   At which English club did Wayne start his professional football career?

600.   In what year did Wayne make his Hearts League debut?

HEARTS IN THE EUROPEAN CUP WINNERS' CUP

601. Which East German side did Hearts demolish 5-1 in a 1976 ECWC match?

602. Who is Hearts' all-time top scorer in the ECWC?

603. Which team eliminated Hearts in the second round in 1976, before going on to win the competition?

604. True or false: Kevin Keegan faced Hearts on ECWC business in 1976?

605. Which former European Champions did Hearts face in an ECWC qualifying round in 1996?

606. Name the two managers that have guided Hearts into ECWC campaigns.

607. What was the aggregate score when Hearts played Estonian side Lantana in 1998?

608. Who scored for Hearts in the 1-1 draw in a 1998 ECWC away leg against Real Mallorca?

609. Following on from the previous question, which area of Mallorca's pitch upset Hearts' officials before the match?

610. What was significant about the Maroons' entry in the 1998/99 ECWC?

WALTER KIDD

611. In which decade did Walter make his Hearts League debut?

612. Following on from the previous question, can you name the Hearts' manager at that time?

613. How many League goals did Walter score for Hearts in his football career – 6, 7 or 8?

614. What nationality is Walter – Irish, English or Scottish?

615. True or false: Walter once managed Hearts in the 1990s?

616. How many times did Walter play against Hibernian in the League during his Hearts career, with Hearts winning on 13 of those occasions – 22, 28 or 34?

617. How many League appearances did Walter make for Hearts in his career - 367, 467 or 567?

618. What was Walter's nickname while at Tynecastle?

619. In what position did Walter play during his playing days?

620. In which year was Walter born – 1958, 1959 or 1960?

HEARTS IN THE 1950s

621. Which team did Hearts defeat 2-1 before of a crowd of 65,860 on 2 January 1950?

622. Following on from the previous question, who scored Hearts' first goal of the 1950s?

623. What was Hearts' lowest end-of-season League position in the 1950s?

624. How many goals did Hearts score in the League match immediately prior to winning the 1956 Scottish Cup?

625. How many competitive goals did Hearts score between (and including) seasons 1949/50 and 1959/60 - 997, 1,066, or 1,252?

626. Which Glasgow team did the Maroons beat 5-0 in a League Cup tie on 9 August 1952?

627. How many points did Hearts finish behind Champions Rangers in season 1958/59?

628. How many days elapsed between Hearts' 1956 Scottish Cup final win and their next League match, against Motherwell?

629. Which former England Under-23 international goal keeper made his Hearts debut in 1956 in a 3-2 win against Kilmarnock?

630. Which former Hibs star scored Hearts' final goal of the 1950s, in a 3-0 win over Dundee?

JOHN COLQUHOUN

631. In which year was John born in Stirling – 1963, 1964 or 1965?

632. How many playing spells did John have at Hearts during his playing days?

633. True or false: John was a full international for Scotland?

634. From which club did John sign in 1985 to join the Jam Tarts?

635. How many League appearances did John make for Hearts in his career- 246, 346 or 446?

636. To which team did Hearts lose 5-1 in the 1996 Scottish Cup final, with John scoring the only goal for the Jam Tarts?

637. In which two positions did John mostly play during his playing days?

638. What is John's middle name – Mark, Michael or Martyn?

639. From which club did John sign in 1993 to join Hearts for the second time?

640. How many League goals did John score for Hearts in his career – 67, 77 or 87?

2005/2006

641. Who became Hearts' manager for the start of season 2005/06?

642. How many of their first eight League games did Hearts win?

643. Which popular Frenchman quickly earned the nick name 'Le Juge'?

644. Which were the only team to defeat a George Burley-led Hearts side?

645. Which former England striker became Hearts' manager in November 2005?

646. How many players made their debut for Hearts during season 2005/06 - 11, 15, or 19?

647. Who were Hearts' joint-top scorers for the season with 17 goals each?

648. Name the three SPL teams that the Jam Tarts defeated on their way to lifting the 2006 Scottish Cup.

649. True or false: Rudi Skácel scored in his first and his last competitive games for Hearts?

650. Which Hearts player was sent off in the 2006 Scottish Cup final?

ALAN McLAREN

651.   What is Alan's middle name – James, John or Joseph?

652.   For which team did Alan sign in 1994 when he left Tynecastle?

653.   Following on from the previous question, how much was the transfer deal worth?

654.   How many full international caps did Alan make for Scotland – 14, 24 or 34?

655.   True or false: Alan had to retire from playing football at the age of 27 due to injury?

656.   Where in Scotland was Alan born in 1971?

657.   How many League appearances did Alan make for Hearts during his playing career – 182, 192 or 202?

658.   In what year did Alan make his Hearts League debut?

659.   Following on from the previous question, which Jam Tarts management duo handed Alan his debut for the club?

660.   How many League goals did Alan score for Hearts during his career – 7, 8 or 9?

DAVE MACKAY – 'LEGEND'

661.   In what year was the legendary Dave born?

662.   In what year did Dave make his debut for the Maroons?

663.   In which season did Dave captain Hearts to a record-breaking League Championship?

664.   How much did Tottenham Hotspur pay for Dave when he left Hearts in 1959 - £12,000, £22,000 or £32,000?

665.   What did Dave inspire Tottenham Hotspur to win in season 1960/61?

666.   Name the Derby County manager who managed to talk Dave out of returning to Tynecastle.

667.   While under Dave's management, how did Derby County fare in the 1974/75 Championship?

668.   Which country did Dave coach between 1978 and 1987?

669.   How many full Scotland caps did Dave win?

670.   In 2006 Dave became an inaugural inductee of what?

SCOTT CRABBE

671. In what position did Scott play during his playing days?

672. True or false: Scott started his professional football career at Hearts?

673. Which club did Scott join when he left Tynecastle in 1992?

674. In which year was Scott born in Edinburgh – 1968, 1969 or 1970?

675. How many League goals did Scott score for Hearts during his career – 29, 31 or 33?

676. With which club did Scott win the First Division during 2000/2001?

677. True or false: Scott won a full international cap for Scotland?

678. Who was the Jam Tarts manager when Scott left Tynecastle?

679. For which Scottish club did Scott play between 1997 and 2000?

680. How many League appearances did Scott make for Hearts in his career - 116, 166 or 216?

LEAGUE CUP WINNERS

681. Up until 2008/09, how many times have Hearts won the League Cup?

682. Hearts' 1954 League Cup win was the club's first major footballing honour since what year?

683. How many goals did King Willie Bauld help himself to in the 1954 League Cup final?

684. How many goals did King Willie Bauld score in the 1958 League Cup final?

685. Name the all the teams that Hearts have beaten in League Cup finals.

686. In what year did Hearts successfully retain the League Cup?

687. Which Hearts player scored in both of those back-to-back League Cup finals?

688. What was the Jam Tarts' biggest win in a League Cup final?

689. Which 'Norrie' scored Hearts' winning goal in the 1962 League Cup final?

690. Which 6ft 4ins referee famously disallowed a late 'goal' against Hearts in the 1962 League Cup final?

PASQUALE BRUNO

691.   In which year was Pasquale born in Lecce, Italy – 1960, 1962 or 1964?

692.   For which English team did Pasquale sign in 1997 when he left Tynecastle, but only played 45 minutes for them before returning home to Italy?

693.   Who was the Jam Tarts' manager when Pasquale made his Hearts debut?

694.   How many League games did Pasquale make for Hearts – 35, 75 or 115?

695.   Which team were Hearts playing when Pasquale was sent off in a 3-0 away defeat during September 1996 in the Premier League?

696.   For which Italian giants did Pasquale play between 1987 and 1990?

697.   In what position did Pasquale mostly play?

698.   Against which team did Pasquale score his only Hearts League goal during his playing career in a 3-1 defeat during November 1995?

699.   True or false: Pasquale won five international caps for Italy during his playing career?

700.   From which Italian team did Pasquale sign when he joined Hearts in 1995?

HEARTS IN THE 1980s

701. In which Division were Hearts playing at the start of the 1980s?

702. In which season did Hearts lose games to Queens Park, East Stirlingshire, Forfar Athletic and Dumbarton?

703. What type of TV show did Wallace Mercer present as a one-off?

704. Which two former Rangers players were made manager and assistant manager of Hearts in 1982?

705. Which company's name became the first to sponsor the famous maroon jersey in 1982?

706. True or false: Hearts qualified for Europe at the end of their Premier League rebirth season, 1983/84?

707. In how many Premier League and Scottish Cup games were Hearts undefeated from October 1985 up until May 1986?

708. Following on from the previous question, at which stadium did Hearts' undefeated run come to a shattering end, losing 2-0?

709. In which other 1980s season did Hearts finish as Premier League runners-up?

710. Who was the Maroons' top goalscorer in the 1980s?

DAVE McPHERSON

711. How many playing spells did Dave have at Tynecastle – 2, 3 or 4?

712. In which year was Dave born in Paisley – 1963, 1964 or 1965?

713. From which team did Dave sign when he joined the Maroons in July 1987?

714. Following on from the previous question, which Hearts management duo signed Dave in July 1987?

715. Against which team did Dave score in a 2-2 home draw in the SPL during October 1996, his only Jam Tarts goal during the 1996/97 season?

716. How many League goals did Dave score for Hearts during his football career – 24, 34 or 44?

717. For which Scottish team did Dave sign in 2001?

718. How many League appearances did Dave make for Hearts in his career – 290, 292 or 294?

719. In what position did Dave play during his playing days?

720. How many full international caps did Dave win during his playing career – 21, 27 or 33?

MISCELLANEOUS - 2

721.   Which part of Julien Brellier's anatomy was subjected to an initial yellow card in a 2006 Champions League qualifying match in Athens?

722.   In 1999, which inspirational midfielder's hip injury was bizarrely alleviated by wearing a gum shield?

723.   Which opposition player publicly goaded Hearts on 16 August 1997 before finding himself on the end of a 4-1 thrashing to Aberdeen?

724.   Which two Hearts players were sent off in a 1994 pre-season friendly for fighting each other?

725.   How many times have Hearts reached the Scottish Cup final in a year ending with a '6'?

726.   Members of which pop group were present to watch Alan Maybury play in 2003 against Hibernian?

727.   In which 2005 British film could former goalkeeper Steve Banks be spotted?

728.   The Maroons reached the final of which TV quiz show in 1970?

729.   Whose match-day MC rallying call is 'Let's make some noise'?

730.   Which actor, famous for playing the gritty Inspector in the TV series Rebus, is a passionate Hearts supporter?

NEIL McCANN

731. In which year was Neil born in Greenock – 1973, 1974 or 1975?

732. How many playing spells has Neil had at Tynecastle – 2, 3 or 4?

733. At which club did Neil start his professional football career in 1992?

734. For which Scottish team did Neil play between 1998 and 2003?

735. How many goals did Neil score for Scotland in his 25 full international caps?

736. Against which club did Neil score a brace in a 3-2 home win in the Premier League during February 1997?

737. Against which club did Neil make his Hearts debut during August 1996, scoring in a 1-1 home draw in the Scottish League Cup?

738. What is the only winners' medal that Neil won as a Hearts player?

739. Which team did Neil sign for when he left Tynecastle in 2008?

740. What is Neil's middle name – Docherty, David or Daniel?

2006/2007

741. After guiding the team to a Scottish Cup success, who was appointed as permanent manager of Hearts before season 2006/07?

742. Which three Hearts players were sent off over two legs against AEK Athens?

743. Who became interim head coach of Hearts on 23 October 2006?

744. Following on from the previous question, how many games did Hearts win under his charge?

745. Who were the so-called 'Riccarton Three'?

746. Who became interim head coach on 2 March 2007?

747. Which two clubs knocked Hearts out of the domestic Cup competitions during 2007/08?

748. What was the score between Hearts and Dundee United on 17 March 2007?

749. How many League points did Hearts take from games against Hibernian during 2006/07?

750. What was the Maroons' final League position at the end of this season?

STEVE FULTON

751. In which year was Steve born in Greenock – 1970, 1971 or 1972?

752. How many League goals did Steve score for Hearts in his career – 15, 18 or 21?

753. From which club did Steve sign for Hearts in 1995?

754. Which Hearts manager brought Steve to the club as one of his first signings?

755. Steve was booked against Hibs on 14 August 1999 for doing what?

756. Against which team did Steve score the winning goal in a 2-1 home SPL win during November 1998?

757. For which team did Steve play during the 2004/05 season?

758. Against which team did Steve score a double on 1 January 1998?

759. With which Scottish team did Steve start his professional football career in 1987?

760. For which team did Steve sign in 2002 when he left Tynecastle?

OTHER COMPETITIONS

761.   Hearts played in the final of the 1919 Victory Cup, that commemorates which war?

762.   Which team did Hearts play in the 1971 final of the inaugural Texaco Cup?

763.   Following on from the previous question, although Hearts lost on aggregate, which Maroons player scored the only goal of the second leg?

764.   Hearts competed in the (by then named) Anglo/Scottish Cup for the last time in which season?

765.   In which season did the Jam Tarts win the First Division?

766.   In which two years did Hearts win the Tennents' Sixes?

767.   Which two teams did Hearts defeat in the finals of the Tennents' Sixes?

768.   In which two years did Hearts and Hibs battle out the Festival Cup?

769.   How many times did Hearts win the Festival Cup?

770.   In which year did a young Hearts team not win the BP Youth Cup - 1993, 1996 or 2000?

COLIN CAMERON

771.   What is Colin's nickname?

772.   From which club did Colin sign when he joined the
       Maroons in 1996?

773.   Against which team did Colin score a brace in a 7-1
       home win in the SPL during February 2001?

774.   Following on from the previous question, can you
       name the other two Hearts players who scored a brace
       in the game?

775.   For which Midlands team did Colin sign in August 2001
       on leaving Tynecastle?

776.   How many goals did Colin score for Hearts during the
       2000/01 season?

777.   Against which club did Colin score a brace in a 2-0
       home win during January 1998 in the SPL?

778.   Which Hearts manager signed Colin for the club in
       1996?

779.   How many goals did Colin score for Scotland in his 28
       full international caps?

780.   In which year was Colin born – 1972, 1974 or 1976?

HEARTS AT MURRAYFIELD

781. Who were Hearts' first ever opponents at Murrayfield?

782. Who scored Hearts' first ever goal at Murrayfield?

783. Which two teams did Hearts face at Murrayfield during the group stages of the 2004/05 UEFA Cup?

784. With which opposition manager did John Robertson have an altercation immediately after Hearts' elimination from the 2004/05 UEFA Cup?

785. Name the three teams that Hearts played in competitive matches at Murrayfield during season 2006/07.

786. Which former Middlesbrough and Rangers player faced Hearts in a Champions League qualifying tie at Murrayfield on 9 August 2006?

787. Which other 'Maroons' did Hearts play on a miserable night at Murrayfield on 14 September 2006?

788. Which two Spanish sides have Hearts faced in friendly matches at Murrayfield?

789. Against which team at Murrayfield did the Jam Tarts record their highest ever 'home' attendance?

790. Which Scottish team lobbied against the prospect of facing Hearts at Murrayfield for a 2006 Scottish Cup semi-final tie?

STÉPHANE ADAM

791. In what position did Stéphane play during his playing days?

792. From which French club did Stéphane join Hearts in 1997?

793. How many League goals did Stéphane score during his Hearts career – 27, 29 or 31?

794. Against which team did Stéphane score his first Hearts goal, in a League match played on 27 September 1997 in a 3-0 win?

795. Against which team did Stéphane score a hat-trick in a 5-3 home win during November 1997?

796. True or false: Stéphane scored Hearts' clincher in the 1998 Scottish Cup final win against Rangers in a 2-1 win?

797. Against which team did Stéphane score a brace in the SPL in a 2-1 home win during December 1998?

798. How many League goals did Stéphane score for Hearts during the 2000/01 season?

799. How many League games did Stéphane play for Hearts in his career – 108, 180 or 280?

800. What is Stéphane's middle name – David, Luke or Lucien?

ROALD 'KNIKSEN' JENSEN

801. In which year was Roald born - 1943, 1945 or 1947?

802. What nationality is Roald?

803. What does 'Kniksen' translate into English as?

804. For which club did Roald play either side of his six-year spell at Hearts?

805. In which ill-fated season did 21-year-old Roald make his Hearts debut?

806. Due to injuries, to how many competitive Hearts appearances was the brilliant Jensen restricted – 99, 102 or 113?

807. How many competitive goals did Roald score for Hearts?

808. In what year did Roald make a one-off guest appearance for Hearts - 1976, 1979 or 1982?

809. How many national caps did Roald win?

810. Outside which stadium is there a statue of Roald Jensen?

THOMAS FLÖGEL

811.   What nationality is Thomas?

812.   Against which team did Thomas make his torrid Hearts League debut in a 3-1 away defeat during August 1997?

813.   Against which team did Thomas make his Hearts home League debut, scoring in a 4-1 win during August 1997?

814.   How many League goals did Thomas score for Hearts in his first season at Tynecastle?

815.   Against which club did Thomas score Hearts' fifth goal in a 5-2 away League win during May 1999?

816.   How many full international caps did Thomas win for his country, scoring 3 goals – 37, 38 or 39?

817.   How many League goals did Thomas score for the Maroons in his career – 9, 19 or 29?

818.   Which Hearts manager signed Thomas for the club in 1997?

819.   For which club did Thomas play before and then after Hearts?

820.   In which year was Thomas born – 1969, 1970 or 1971?

2007/2008

821. Which team paid Hearts a British transfer record fee for a goalkeeper in August 2007?

822. Which two Lithuanian players made their debuts for Hearts against Hibs on 6 August 2007?

823. Who won the Edinburgh derby on 6 August 2007?

824. Which team thrashed Hearts 5-0 on 25 August 2007?

825. Who did Hearts defeat 4-2 at Tynecastle on 15 September 2007?

826. How many games in a row did Hearts lose between 8 December 2007 and 2 January 2008?

827. Who was appointed as caretaker manager of Hearts on 1 January 2008?

828. Which two teams knocked Hearts out of both domestic Cup competitions in January 2008?

829. True or false: 2007/08 was the first time that Hearts had failed to make the 'Top 6' post-SPL split?

830. What was Hearts' final League position at the end of this season?

GILLES ROUSSET

831.   In which year was Gilles born - 1961, 1962 or 1963?

832.   What was the only honour that Gilles won while a Hearts player?

833.   In what year did Gilles join the Jam Tarts?

834.   From which club did Hearts sign Gilles?

835.   What was name of the England striker who failed miserably when trying to lob Gilles at Wembley in 1992?

836.   How many full international caps did Gilles win for France in his career?

837.   True or false: Gilles once scored a League goal for Hearts during his career?

838.   To which team did Hearts lose 2-1 during November 1999 in the SPL, when Gilles was sent off after 40 minutes?

839.   Which Hearts manager signed Gilles for the club?

840.   How many League games did Gilles play for Hearts in his career – 132, 152 or 182?

JIM JEFFERIES

841. In which year was Jim born – 1950, 1952 or 1954?

842. True or false: Jim was born in the East Lothian town of Haddington?

843. In what year did Jim make his competitive debut for Hearts?

844. True or false: all of Jim's appearances for Hearts were made in the 1970s?

845. Which team did Jim join after leaving Hearts as a player?

846. In what year did Jim leave Falkirk to become manager of Hearts?

847. What is the name of the Falkirk owner who desperately tried to persuade Jim to stay at Brockville?

848. Why was Jim unable to attend the match at Motherwell on 21 February 1998?

849. How many European campaigns did Hearts have during Jim's tenure as manager?

850. How many major honours did Jim lead Hearts to when he was manager?

ANTTI NIEMI

851. In what year did Antti join Hearts from Rangers?

852. With which English team did Antti finish his career, retiring in 2008?

853. True or false: Antti once played for Celtic during his playing days?

854. What is Antti's middle name – Mikko, Mika or Mini?

855. Against which team did Antti make his Hearts League debut in a 3-0 home defeat?

856. How many League appearances did Antti make for Hearts during his career – 89, 99 or 109?

857. In which year was Antti born – 1972, 1974 or 1976?

858. For which country did Antti win 67 full international caps?

859. Which manager signed Antti for Hearts?

860. Which English team did Antti join when he left Tynecastle in 2002?

WHO AM I? - 1

861. I played 467 games for Hearts between 1964 and 1976. Away from football I ran The Pivot Bar in Infirmary Street.

862. I'm a 'no nonsense' Finnish midfielder who played 25 games for Hearts during season 2001/02.

863. I made 56 appearances for Hearts between 1980 and 1982, scoring 16 goals. My brother is Hearts' all-time top League goalscorer.

864. Between 1998 and 2001 I scored 30 goals for Hearts. I also scored in the Champions League for Rangers.

865. As the triumphant captain of Hearts, I raised the Scottish Cup aloft in front of 133,583 people.

866. I'm a Slovakian goalkeeper who signed for Hearts from FBK Kaunas in 2008.

867. Born in Edinburgh in 1955, I played 114 games for Hearts in three years between 1974 and 1977 before spending eight years at Hibernian.

868. Born in 1980, I'm a Hearts fan who played 13 games for the club between 1998 and 2000, scoring goals against St Johnstone and IBV Vestmannaeyja.

869. Born in Bellshill in 1966, I played 150 games for the Maroons in midfield between 1991 and 1996, scoring 25 goals.

870. I played 84 games for Hearts between 1984 and 1991. You may well remember my goal celebration at Pittodrie with Scott Crabbe!

STEVEN PRESSLEY

871. Which manager signed Steven for the Jam Tarts in 1998?

872. True or false: Steven scored on his Hearts League debut during August 1998?

873. Following on from the previous question, against which team were Hearts playing, winning 2-0?

874. Against which German side did Steven score his only competitive goal for Hearts during the 2000/01 season, in the UEFA Cup 1st round, 2nd leg in September 2000?

875. How many full international caps did Steven win for Scotland during his playing career?

876. Which Scottish team did Steven join in 2009?

877. What is Steven's nickname?

878. What is Steven's middle name – John, James or Jason?

879. Against which team did Steven score an 88th-minute penalty to clinch a 2-1 away win in the SPL during March 2002?

880. Which club did Steven join in December 2006 when he left Tynecastle?

CLASSIC MATCH 1995 – HEARTS 4, RANGERS 2

881. Who was the manager of Hearts for this scintillating match?

882. Can you name the four Hearts goalscorers?

883. Can you name the Hearts and the Rangers goalkeepers?

884. Who were the two goalscorers for Rangers?

885. True or false: John Millar was sent off for Hearts?

886. Which 35-year-old was the oldest member of Hearts' starting line-up?

887. Which Maroons player went on a breathtaking last-minute run to set up the fourth goal?

888. True or false: Sky TV broadcast the game live to a UK-wide audience?

889. Which three players in the Hearts line-up went on to manage the club?

890. Which team brought Hearts' Scottish Cup run to a humbling end, with Hearts losing 1-0?

RUDI SKÁCEL

891.   What nationality is Rudi?

892.   Against which team did Rudi score a stunning brace for Hearts in a 2-1 home win in the SPL during December 2005?

893.   True or false: Rudi scored on his Hearts debut in the SPL during July 2005?

894.   Following on from the previous question, which team did Hearts beat 4-2 away on Rudi's debut?

895.   True or false: Rudi scored in each of his first seven League games for Hearts?

896.   How many League goals did Rudi score for Hearts during 2005/06?

897.   In which year was Rudi born – 1978, 1979 or 1980?

898.   Against which team did Rudi make his Hearts home debut during August 2005, scoring in a 4-0 home win?

899.   Which manager signed Rudi for the Maroons in 2005?

900.   From which club was Rudi on loan when he joined Hearts in 2005?

'22 IN A ROW'

901. What calendar years did Hearts' '22 in a row' of undefeated games span?

902. Who scored the first goal for Hearts in their '22 in a row' in a 2-1 win over Hibernian?

903. Of the 22 undefeated games, how many did Hearts win?

904. Can you name the striker and the defender who both played in 21 of the 22 undefeated games?

905. How many goals did John Robertson score during '22 in a row'?

906. Which Hibernian goalkeeper kept the scoreline respectable with a series of spectacular saves on 23 March 1991 in a 3-1 win?

907. Who scored the winning goal to make it '21 in a row' in a 2-1 win?

908. What made the 'Happy 21st' party different from the other games in the long, unbeaten run?

909. Which former Jam Tart played 20 games for Hibernian during '22 in a row'?

910. Name the three managers who guided Hearts through '22 in a row'.

PAUL HARTLEY

911.   From which club did Paul sign to join Hearts in 2003?

912.   Against which club did Paul score his first Hearts goal, in a 1-1 away draw during September 2003?

913.   Against which team did Paul score a brace in a 2-1 Hearts win in the Scottish League Cup 3rd round during September 2004?

914.   In which year was Paul born – 1975, 1976 or 1977?

915.   At which Scottish club did Paul begin his professional football career in 1994?

916.   How many goals did Paul score for Hearts during 2004/05?

917.   What is Paul's middle name – Justin, Jeremy or James?

918.   Against which team did Paul score his final Hearts goal in a Boxing Day 3-2 home win, the goal coming just two minutes into the game?

919.   In what year did Paul leave Tynecastle?

920.   Which team did Paul join when he left Hearts?

2008/2009

921. Who was named as the new manager of Hearts on 11 July 2008?

922. Who became assistant manager of Hearts on 5 August 2008?

923. Which Ugandan international joined Hearts from the South African side, Kaiser Chiefs?

924. Which Danish striker was signed on loan from Italian side, Reggina?

925. Which club did captain Christophe Berra join in January 2009?

926. Whose first-half goal sent the Maroons on their way to Scottish Cup victory over Hibs?

927. Hearts kicked off the campaign with a game against Motherwell. What was the score?

928. Who scored a magnificent second-half solo goal against Falkirk on 22 November 2008?

929. Who scored Hearts' goals in the 2-2 draw at Ibrox on 21 March 2009?

930. True or false: Saulius Mikoliūnas scored the winner in Hearts' first three home games?

ANDRIUS VELIČKA

931. In which year was Andrius born – 1978, 1979 or 1980?

932. What nationality is Andrius, who won his first full international cap in 1998?

933. In what year did Andrius join the Jam Tarts on loan?

934. Against which team did Andrius make his Hearts debut in a 1-0 defeat?

935. Against which team did Andrius score a hat-trick in a 4-0 Scottish Cup win during January 2007?

936. For which Scottish team did Andrius sign in 2008 from Viking FK?

937. In what position does Andrius play?

938. Against which team did Andrius score his first Hearts goals, a brace in a 2-2 away draw in the SPL during October 2006?

939. Against which team did Andrius score a brace in a 2-0 Hearts away win in the Scottish League Cup quarter-final during October 2007?

940. Against which team did Andrius score a brace in a 2-0 Hearts home win in the SPL during February 2008?

WHO AM I? - 2

941.   I played 98 games for Hearts between 2002 and 2006, but it wasn't until I joined Queen of the South that I played in a Scottish Cup final.

942.   I played just 45 games for Hearts at left back between 1967 and 1968 before my form earned me a £65,000 move to Manchester City.

943.   I played for Celtic and Rangers before moving to Hearts from Everton in 1993.

944.   Between 1984 and 1990 I played 208 games for Hearts as a left back and occasional centre half. I scored against Celtic in a Scottish Cup semi-final.

945.   I played 173 games for Hearts between 1999 and 2004 before seeking a move to the Premiership. I ended up at Aberdeen.

946.   I'm a skilful Jamaican striker who played 29 games for the Maroons during season 2001/02.

947.   I scored 128 goals for Hearts in just 239 games before moving to Celtic, becoming an integral part of the 'Lisbon Lions'.

948.   I'm from Loanhead and I won a Scottish Cup medal with Hearts aged just 19 before eventually earning a move to Everton. I am not Alex Young.

949.   My last-gasp equalising goal against Celtic sparked a pitch invasion in 1998.

950.   I am a Bosnian striker and played just nine games for Hearts in 1989. I found it difficult to adjust to the Scottish game, but even I still managed to score a winner against Hibs!

ANDREW DRIVER

951.   What is Andrew's middle name – David, Daniel or Dominic?

952.   What squad number did Andrew wear for Hearts during the 2008/09 season?

953.   Against which team did Andrew score Hearts' winning goal in a 2-1 away SPL win during August 2008?

954.   In which year was Andrew born in Oldham – 1985, 1986 or 1987?

955.   How many League goals did Andrew score for Hearts during the 2007/08 season?

956.   In what position does Andrew play?

957.   Which manager handed Andrew a place on the bench for Hearts' final League game of season 2003/04?

958.   Against which team did Andrew score his first goal for the club, a spectacular volley, on his debut on 26 August 2006?

959.   True or false: Andrew scored a hat-trick for Hearts during the 2008/09 season?

960.   Andrew scored Hearts' first goal after 40 minutes in a 3-1 away win against St Mirren in the SPL during September 2007, but which two other Hearts players scored?

WHERE DID THEY COME FROM? - 2

Match up the player with the club he left to join Hearts

961.	Ramón Pereira	Rangers
962.	Roddy MacDonald	Juventude
963.	David Holt	Atalanta
964.	Samuel Camazzola	PAOK Salonika
965.	Jimmy Bone	Celtic
966.	Rab McKinnon	Queens Park
967.	David Kirkwood	Barcelona
968.	Stefano Salvatori	Raith Rovers
969.	Juanjo	Hong Kong Rangers
970.	Hristos Karipidis	FC Twente

LARYEA 'LARRY' KINGSTON

971. Which Hearts manager gave Larry his debut for the Maroons?

972. For which country is Larry a full international?

973. What squad number did Larry wear for Hearts during the 2008/09 season?

974. Can you name Larry's brother, also a professional footballer and a full international goalkeeper?

975. True or false: Larry was initially on loan at Tynecastle before signing on a permanent basis?

976. Against which side did Larry score his first Hearts goal in his second League match for the club, a 1-1 home draw during February 2007?

977. How many League goals did Larry score for Hearts during the 2007/08 season?

978. Against which team did Larry score the winning goal in the 81st minute in a 3-2 SPL home win during April 2008?

979. From which Russian team did Larry sign when he joined the Jam Tarts?

980. Against which team did Larry make his Hearts debut, in a 1-0 Scottish Cup defeat during February 2007?

JOHN ROBERTSON – 'THE HAMMER OF HIBS'

981. In what year was John Grant Robertson born – 1960, 1962 or 1964?

982. Which team unsuccessfully tried to pressure the young Robbo into signing a contract with them before he joined Hearts?

983. In what year did Robbo make his debut for the Jam Tarts?

984. For which English team did Robbo play briefly?

985. In which season did Robbo record his highest goal tally, with 31 goals?

986. How many competitive games did Robbo play for Hearts – 566, 602 or 631?

987. How many competitive goals did Robbo score for Hearts – 249, 271 or 299?

988. How many goals did Robbo score against Hibernian?

989. How many Scotland caps did Robbo win?

990. After 17 incredible years, what was Robbo's final duty as a Hearts player?

MICHAEL STEWART

991. In which year was Michael born in Edinburgh – 1981, 1983 or 1985?

992. From which rivals did Michael sign to join Hearts on a permanent basis in July 2007?

993. Against which team did Michael make his Jam Tarts debut during August 2004 in a 1-0 away win?

994. What squad number did Michael wear during the 2008/09 season?

995. What team does Michael support – Hearts, Aberdeen or Dundee?

996. Against which team did Michael score his first Hearts goal, in a 1-1 away draw during August 2007?

997. True or false: Michael was sent off twice during his 2007/08 season with Hearts?

998. Against which team did Michael score Hearts' first goal of the 2008/09 League season, in a 3-2 home win on the opening day of the season?

999. How many League goals did Michael score for Hearts during the 2007/08 SPL season?

1000. For which English team did Michael play in the Champions League during 2003?

ANSWERS

CLUB HISTORY

1. 1874
2. The Meadows
3. Tom Purdie
4. 1890
5. Hibernian
6. Maroon and white
7. 15
8. Tynecastle
9. The First World War
10. Jam Tarts

MANAGERS OF HEARTS

11. John McCartney
12. Sandy Clark
13. Bobby Moncur
14. False: it was season 1994/95
15. Romania
16. Sandy Jardine
17. Jim Jefferies
18. Willie Ormond
19. David McLean
20. John Robertson

GARY MACKAY - 'MR HEARTS'

21. 1964
22. Tynecastle High School
23. 1980
24. 1997
25. 5ft 9in
26. Bulgaria
27. Republic of Ireland
28. Inverness Caledonian

29. Airdrieonians
30. True

WHERE DID THEY GO? - 1

31.	Willie Jamieson	Ayr United
32.	Stephen Simmons	Dunfermline Athletic
33.	Roman Bednář	West Bromwich Albion
34.	Jeremy Goss	Colchester United
35.	Iain Jardine	Partick Thistle
36.	Darren Jackson	Livingston
37.	Jim Townsend	Morton
38.	Andy Webster	Wigan Athletic
39.	Alan Gordon	Dundee United
40.	Tosh McKinlay	Celtic

GREAT GAMES

41. José Quitongo
42. 2-2
43. Andrew Driver, Ibrahim Tall, Michael Stewart and Kestutis Ivaškevičius
44. Aberdeen
45. René Moller
46. Willie Bauld
47. Hearts 6, Dundee 3
48. Gary McSwegan
49. Love Street (St Mirren)
50. Rudi Skácel and Roman Bednář

WHERE DID THEY GO? – 2

51.	Ian Baird	Bristol City
52.	Roy Barry	Dunfermline Athletic
53.	Dennis Wyness	Inverness Caledonian Thistle
54.	Gary Locke	Bradford City

55.	Neil Berry	Falkirk
56.	David Bowman	Coventry City
57.	Fitzroy Simpson	Walsall
58.	Bobby Kirk	Gala Fairydean
59.	Derek Ferguson	Sunderland
60.	Cammy Fraser	Dundee

CRAIG GORDON

61. 1982
62. Balerno Community High School
63. Cowdenbeath
64. Livingston
65. FC Girondins de Bordeaux
66. David Clarkson
67. Derek Townsley
68. Fabien Barthez
69. Gianluigi Buffon
70. Trinidad and Tobago

HEARTS IN THE SPL

71. Stéphane Adam
72. 6th
73. Hibs were playing in the First Division
74. Gordan Petrić, Antti Niemi, Fitzroy Simpson and Róbert Tomaschek
75. Gary Wales
76. Andy Kirk
77. False: it was the other way around
78. Celtic and Livingston
79. Jean-Louis Valois
80. Alan Maybury

WHERE DID THEY COME FROM - 1?

81.	Gordon Durie	Rangers
82.	Stéphane Mahé	Celtic
83.	Graeme Hogg	Portsmouth
84.	Ian Crawford	Hamilton Academical
85.	Steven Boyack	Dundee
86.	Neil Pointon	Oldham Athletic
87.	Frank Liddell	Alloa Athletic
88.	Eddie Thomson	Penicuik Athletic
89.	Steve Banks	Gillingham
90.	Peter Marinello	Phoenix Inferno

TOP LEAGUE GOALSCORERS

91. Barney Battles
92. Andy Black
93. Jimmy Wardhaugh
94. Willie Wallace
95. False: it was Donald Ford
96. True
97. 1987/88
98. Jim Hamilton
99. Gary McSwegan
100. 2002/03 and 2003/04

DREW BUSBY – THE BUZZ BOMB

101. 1947
102. False: he was born in Glasgow
103. It was the Glasgow club's last goal before going out of business
104. Airdrieonians
105. 1973
106. £35,000
107. Sparta Rotterdam

108. *256*
109. *84*
110. *1979*

TYNECASTLE STADIUM
111. *1886*
112. *£12,000*
113. *53,396*
114. *1978*
115. *Luís Figo*
116. *The Shed*
117. *The School End*
118. *The Wheatfield Stand*
119. *The 500 Club*
120. *10,000*

HEARTS IN THE EUROPEAN CUP
121. *Standard Liege, 5 Hearts 1*
122. *Ian Crawford*
123. *Hearts 2, Standard Liege 1*
124. *Benfica. They won the tournament in season 1960/61*
125. *Alex Young*
126. *False: he didn't join Benfica until 1961*
127. *NK Široki Brijeg*
128. *Ibrahim Tall and Roman Bednář*
129. *Saulius Mikoliūnas*
130. *False: but 18-year-old Jamie Mole did*

HAT-TRICK HEROES
131. *Alex Young*
132. *John Colquhoun*
133. *St Mirren*
134. *Andrius Velička*

135.   *His first*

136.   *Jock White*

137.   *Stéphane Adam*

138.   *Juho Makela*

139.   *Gary McSwegan*

140.   *Donald Ford*

MISCELLANEOUS - 1

141.   *They all played in goal for Hearts*

142.   *Aston Villa, Bolton Wanderers, Greenock Morton, Hamilton Academical and Macclesfield Town*

143.   *Kevin Keegan*

144.   *Justin Fashanu*

145.   *Roy Keane*

146.   *His teammate José Gonçalves*

147.   *Adrian Boothroyd*

148.   *True*

149.   *Tomas Brolin*

150.   *Tottenham Hotspur*

LATE, LATE GOALS

151.   *False: it was Willie Jamieson*

152.   *Neil Janczyk*

153.   *John Robertson*

154.   *Graeme Weir*

155.   *Rangers*

156.   *Rubén Palazuelos*

157.   *Austin McCann*

158.   *José Quitongo*

159.   *Sandy Clark*

160.   *Paul Hartley*

BOBBY WALKER – 'THE GREATEST EVER'

161. *False: he was born in 1879*
162. *Edinburgh*
163. *True: he played three games*
164. *'The Walker Final'*
165. *Hearts 4, Celtic 3*
166. *1906*
167. *141*
168. *1913*
169. *He became a director at Hearts*
170. *King Haakon of Norway*

BIG WINS

171. *Hearts 8, Hibs 3*
172. *Róbert Tomaschek - he only scored once*
173. *False: John Robertson scored twice*
174. *Airdrieonians*
175. *Callum Elliot*
176. *Willie Gibson and Drew Busby*
177. *Huntly*
178. *Kings Park*
179. *1957/58*
180. *Hibernians 2, Heart of Mid-Lothian 10*

HEARTS IN THE 1960s

181. *Alex Young*
182. *False: they were the Champions*
183. *By 0.04 of a goal*
184. *Rangers*
185. *Dunfermline Athletic*
186. *Internazionale (Italy)*
187. *12th*
188. *Lausanne*

189. Ernie Winchester

190. Jim Townsend

INTERNATIONAL CAPS

191. 5

192. 5

193. 32

194. 21

195. 23

196. 1

197. 16

198. 2

199. 1

200. 4

2003/2004

201. Dennis Wyness, Paul Hartley and Joe Hamill

202. Patrick Kisnorbo

203. Christophe Berra

204. Alan Maybury, with 40 appearances

205. Mark de Vries

206. They were both own goals

207. Andy Kirk

208. Joe Hamill

209. 3rd

210. It became the highest points tally in the club's history

HOW MUCH DID THEY COST?

211.	Mike Galloway	£60,000
212.	Ian Baird	£350,000
213.	Jim Weir	£300,000
214.	Michal Pospíšil	£300,000
215.	Kevin McKenna	£300,000

216.	Derek Ferguson	£750,000
217.	Kenny Black	£30,000
218.	Alan Maybury	£100,000
219.	Willie Pettigrew	£120,000
220.	Mirsad Bešlija	£850,000

THE TERRIBLE TRIO

221. Alfie Conn, Willie Bauld and Jimmy Wardhaugh
222. Jimmy Wardhaugh
223. Hearts 6, East Fife 1
224. Willie Bauld, with 277 goals
225. Alfie Conn and Jimmy Wardhaugh
226. They scored all five goals
227. Willie Bauld
228. All three of them scored
229. Jimmy Wardhaugh
230. Willie Bauld

PLAYERS' NATIONALITIES - 1

231.	Christian Nadé	French
232.	Peter Van de Ven	Dutch
233.	Nerijus Barasa	Lithuanian
234.	Colin Miller	Canadian
235.	David Obua	Ugandan
236.	Alex Massie	Scottish
237.	José Quitongo	Angolan
238.	René Moller	Danish
239.	Darren Beckford	English
240.	Bruno Aguiar	Portuguese

CLASSIC MATCH 1976 – HEARTS 5, LOCOMOTIV LEIPZIG 1

241. The European Cup Winners' Cup
242. Locomotiv Leipzig, 2 Hearts 0

243. **Willie Gibson**

244. **Roy Kay, Jim Brown and Drew Busby**

245. **Jim Cruickshank**

246. **John Hagart**

247. **On the subs bench**

248. **Ralph Callachan**

249. **All 13 players were Scottish**

250. **SV Hamburg**

PLAYERS' NATIONALITIES - 2

251.	**Samuel Camazzola**	**Brazilian**
252.	**Tepi Moilanen**	**Finnish**
253.	**Mauricio Pinilla**	**Chilean**
254.	**Anthony Basso**	**French**
255.	**Roman Bednář**	**Czech**
256.	**Juanjo**	**Spanish**
257.	**Takis Fyssas**	**Greek**
258.	**Jamie Mole**	**English**
259.	**Basil Colombo**	**Scottish**
260.	**Eggert Jónsson**	**Icelandic**

HEART-BREAKING MOMENTS

261. **Kilmarnock**

262. **Albert Kidd**

263. **Andy Davis**

264. **Gerry Evans**

265. **19th**

266. **Aberdeen**

267. **1 January 1973**

268. **Christophe Berra**

269. **Paul Gascoigne**

270. **Gary Locke**

PLAYER OF THE YEAR

271. John Robertson

272. Edgaras Jankauskas

273. Sandy Jardine

274. Stéphane Paille

275. Craig Levein

276. Dave Mackay

277. Paddy Byrne

278. Lee Wallace

279. Roman Bednář

280. False: it was Craig Gordon

TOMMY WALKER OBE

281. Livingston Station

282. 1932

283. Arsenal

284. The ball twice blew off the spot

285. England 0, Scotland 1

286. False: he scored 205 competitive goals for Hearts

287. Chelsea (1946-48)

288. 15 years, 1951-66

289. 7

290. 1980

HEARTS v. HIBS

291. True: Christmas Day 1875

292. 4

293. Jean-Louis Valois

294. Derek O'Connor

295. 2 (4-1 win in 1973 and a 2-1 win in 1978)

296. 3 (2-1 defeat in 1987, 2-1 defeat in 1988 and a 1-0 defeat in 1989)

297. False: Hearts have the better record both home and away

298.   *Zibi Malkowski*

299.   *The noise of the crowd*

300.   *Gary Glen*

LEAGUE CHAMPIONS

301.   *4*

302.   *1894/95, 1896/97, 1957/58 and 1959/60*

303.   *Promotion*

304.   *Hibernian*

305.   *132*

306.   *1*

307.   *13*

308.   *7*

309.   *True: Hearts scored 102 League goals*

310.   *Kilmarnock*

HEARTS v. RANGERS

311.   *Tommy White*

312.   *Allan Johnston*

313.   *Tommy Murray*

314.   *4 (3 League games and 1 Scottish Cup game)*

315.   *Roman Bednář*

316.   *Ally McCoist*

317.   *Hearts 4, Rangers 0*

318.   *Alex MacDonald*

319.   *Christos Karipidis*

320.   *Sandy Jardine. Hearts won 3-0*

HEARTS IN THE 1990s

321.   *Airdrieonians and Rangers*

322.   *George Wright*

323.   *Hearts 2, Hibs 0*

324.   *1991/92*

325. Alex MacDonald (up to 1990), Joe Jordan (1990-93), Sandy Clark (1993-94), Tommy McLean (1994-95) and Jim Jefferies (1995-2000)

326. Bukta (up to 1991), Admiral (1991-93), Asics (1993-95), Pony (1995-97) and Olympic Sports (1997-2000)

327. Neil Pointon, Gilles Rousset, Pasquale Bruno and Hans Eskilsson

328. Pasquale Bruno, David Weir, Neil Pointon and Paul Ritchie

329. Rousset, McPherson, Naysmith, Weir, Ritchie, Salvatori, McCann, Fulton, Adam, Cameron and Flögel

330. 10th (bottom)

HEARTS v. CELTIC

331. Roman Bednář

332. 3-3

333. Alan McLaren and Tosh McKinlay

334. He was stretchered off with a suspected broken neck

335. Stéphane Adam

336. John Robertson

337. False: as of June 2009, Hearts have never faced any British team in Europe

338. Willie Gibson

339. Bruno Aguiar

340. Scott Crabbe and John Millar

DONALD FORD

341. Linlithgow

342. 1964

343. Accountancy

344. 143

345. 8

346. 3

347. Cricket

348. Falkirk
349. False: he was in the squad but never played
350. Landscape photography

HEARTS v. ABERDEEN

351. Allan Johnston
352. Calum Elliot
353. Aberdeen 0, Hearts 1
354. 35
355. Hearts 3, Aberdeen 0
356. Kevin McKenna
357. Christian Nadé
358. 13
359. Walter Kidd
360. Andrew Driver, Andrius Velička, Ibrahim Tall and Christian Nadé

SCOTTISH CUP WINNERS

361. 7
362. 1891
363. Celtic (in 1901 and 1956)
364. It was held in Edinburgh; the only time the final has been staged outside Glasgow
365. Heart of Mid-Lothian 3, Hibernians 1
366. Ian Crawford
367. Stéphane Adam
368. Thomas Flögel, Stefano Salvatori, Takis Fyssas and Ibrahim Tall
369. Grant Murray and John Robertson (1998); Steve Banks and Christophe Berra (2006)
370. Robbie Neilson

HEARTS v. DUNDEE UNITED

371. Jim Irvine

372. 1984
373. True: 1985-97
374. John Colquhoun
375. Hearts 6, Dundee United 0
376. 1988/89
377. John Robertson
378. True: Dundee United were mostly a Division 2 side until
      1960
379. Michael Stewart
380. John Robertson

2004/2005

381. 13 (Ramon Pereira, Michael Stewart, Jamie McAllister, Craig
      Sives, Callum Elliot, Lee Miller, Saulius Mikoliunas, Hjalmar
      Thorarinsson, Mark Burchill, Lee Wallace, Marius Kizys,
      Deividas Cesnauskis and Jason Thomson)
382. Lee Miller, Neil MacFarlane, Mark Burchill, Hjálmar
      Thórarinsson, Saulius Mikoliūnas, Deividas Česnauskis, Lee
      Wallace and Jamie McAllister
383. Craig Gordon, with 53 appearances
384. Paul Hartley
385. Ruud Gullit
386. Peter Houston
387. Schalke 04
388. Lee Miller and Mark Burchill
389. Vladimir Romanov
390. Sotirios Kyriakos

LEAGUE POSITIONS – 1

391.	1983/84	5th
392.	1896/97	1st
393.	2001/02	5th
394.	1966/67	11th

395.	1959/60	1st
396.	1980/81	10th
397.	1975/76	5th
398.	1956/57	2nd
399.	2005/06	2nd
400.	1991/92	2nd

JOHN CUMMING – 'THE IRON MAN'

401.	1930
402.	Carluke
403.	Celtic
404.	7
405.	None
406.	505
407.	44
408.	9
409.	1967
410.	He got on with the game

HEARTS – THE EARLY YEARS

411.	Dancing
412.	Powburn
413.	Darwen
414.	Vale of Leven
415.	Hearts 21, Anchor 0; the club's record victory
416.	Anderson's
417.	Hibs
418.	True: 1891, 1896, 1901 and 1906
419.	Bolton Wanderers
420.	False: it was the world record fee of its day (£2,500)

CLASSIC MATCH 1989 - HEARTS 1, BAYERN MUNICH 0

| 421. | Iain Ferguson |

422. The School End

423. Tosh McKinlay

424. Henry Smith, Iain Ferguson and Eamonn Bannon

425. Alan McLaren

426. Wayne Foster (English)

427. 26,294

428. Bayern Munich 2, Hearts 0

429. Klaus Augenthaler

430. SSC Napoli (whose midfield included Diego Maradona)

LEAGUE POSITIONS – 2

431.	1987/88	2nd
432.	1997/98	3rd
433.	1953/54	2nd
434.	1914/15	2nd
435.	1994/95	6th
436.	1969/70	4th
437.	1957/58	1st
438.	1976/77	9th
439.	1894/95	1st
440.	1999/2000	3rd

'THE YO-YO YEARS' - 1977-1983

441. 3

442. 1977, 1979 and 1981

443. True

444. 1981/82

445. Dundee

446. Frank Liddell

447. Celtic 6, Hearts 0

448. Forfar Athletic

449. Wallace Mercer

450. Alex MacDonald

IN WHAT YEAR DID WE SIGN?

451.	David Weir	1996
452.	Alan Anderson	1963
453.	Johnny Hamilton	1955
454.	Robbie Neilson	1996
455.	Willie Gibson	1971
456.	Steven Pressley	1998
457.	Neil Berry	1984
458.	Stevie Fulton	1995
459.	Gary Locke	1990
460.	Jim Brown	1967

JIM CRUICKSHANK

461. Glasgow
462. 1960
463. 1977
464. Ayr United
465. 4th
466. 5ft 11ins
467. Queens Park Rangers
468. West Germany
469. 6
470. Joe Davis

GREAT GOALKEEPERS

471. Jack Harkness MBE
472. Henry Smith
473. Willie Duff
474. Scotland 0, England 0
475. False (Gordon Marshall, 267 and Kenny Garland, 132)
476. '3 Fingers'
477. Antti Niemi
478. János Balogh

479. Partick Thistle

480. Gilles Rousset

HEARTS IN THE 1970s

481. Eric Carruthers

482. No one: it was a 0-0 draw

483. Neil Murray

484. 1972/73

485. Hearts 4, Hibernian 1

486. False: Hearts finished 5th

487. It was scored before the official three o'clock kick-off time

488. Des O'Sullivan

489. 1976/77

490. Donald Ford and Jim Cruickshank

CLASSIC MATCH - SCOTTISH CUP FINAL 1998

491. Robert Duvall

492. Steve Fulton

493. Colin Cameron

494. Stéphane Adam

495. Thomas Flögel

496. Jim Hamilton

497. David Weir

498. Grant Murray

499. Open-top bus

500. True: since 1998 only a replica trophy has left Hampden

'H-E-A ...' - GREAT SONGS FROM THE TERRACES

501. 'Massey and Walker and Bauld and MacKay'

502. '... wrong'

503. 'White Christmas'

504. 'The Channel Tunnel'

505. 'Portobelly'

506.   Marshalls

507.   'Super' Wayne Foster

508.   Drew Busby

509.   'The Hibees'

510.   'Hey Jude'

CLASSIC MATCH 2006 - HIBERNIAN 0, HEARTS 4

511.   Scottish FA Cup (semi-final)

512.   Paul Hartley

513.   Edgaras Jankauskas

514.   Ivan Sproule and Gary Smith

515.   Hampden Park, Glasgow

516.   Zbigniew Malkowski

517.   1-0 to Hearts

518.   Stuart Dougal

519.   43,180

520.   Valdas Ivanauskas

WILLIE BAULD – 'THE KING'

521.   1928

522.   Newcraighall

523.   True: he's ranked 10th

524.   Russell Logan

525.   277

526.   3

527.   3

528.   17

529.   3

530.   True: they were all gained in 1950

CLASSIC MATCH – SCOTTISH CUP FINAL 2006

531.   Gretna

532.   1-1

533.   Paul Hartley

534.   Rudi Skácel

535.   Hampden Park, Glasgow

536.   Michal Pospíšil, Julien Brellier and Saulius Mikoliūnas

537.   Craig Gordon

538.   Partick Thistle

539.   51,232

540.   4-2

HEARTS IN THE UEFA CUP

541.   Dukla Prague, Slavia Prague and Sparta Prague

542.   1984

543.   3-0 v. Velež Mostar

544.   0-4 v. Paris St Germain

545.   Henry Smith, with 22 appearances

546.   St Patricks Athletic, Austria Vienna, Velež Mostar and Bayern Munich

547.   True

548.   Sporting Braga, Feyenoord, Schalke 04, FC Basel and Ferencváros

549.   John Robertson, with seven goals

550.   Mark de Vries

CRAIG LEVEIN

551.   William

552.   Scottish PFA Young Player of the Year

553.   2000

554.   16

555.   Cowdenbeath

556.   15

557.   1983

558.   Alex MacDonald

559.   326: 322 (4)

560.   Central defender (he started as a midfielder)

'FORGOTTEN' PLAYERS
561.   Robbie Horn
562.   Tommy Wilson
563.   Myles Hogarth
564.   Tiago Costa
565.   David Dunn and John Knox
566.   Alan Redpath
567.   Gregor Stevens
568.   Mohamed Berthe
569.   Marius Kižys
570.   Stéphane Paille

SANDY JARDINE
571.   Sweeper
572.   1982
573.   1980s: 1986-88
574.   1
575.   9
576.   187
577.   William
578.   False: he only ever co-managed Hearts
579.   3
580.   1948

HENRY SMITH
581.   1956
582.   True
583.   700
584.   1981
585.   Leeds United
586.   Maurice Malpas

587. Tommy Coyne

588. 3

589. 1995

590. False: he missed one

'SUPER' WAYNE FOSTER

591. Striker

592. 1963

593. 4

594. Alex MacDonald

595. Partick Thistle

596. 12

597. Hibernian

598. 160: 115 (45)

599. Bolton Wanderers

600. 1986

HEARTS IN THE EUROPEAN CUP WINNERS' CUP

601. Locomotiv Leipzig

602. Willie Gibson

603. SV Hamburg

604. False: Keegan didn't join SV Hamburg until the following year

605. Red Star Belgrade

606. John Hagart and Jim Jefferies

607. Hearts won 6-0 on aggregate

608. Jim Hamilton

609. A large hump on the goal line

610. It was the last ever campaign into the competition by a Scottish club

WALTER KIDD

611. 1970s

612. *Willie Ormond*

613. *6*

614. *Scottish*

615. *False: he never managed Hearts*

616. *22*

617. *367: 344 (23)*

618. *Zico*

619. *Right back*

620. *1958*

HEARTS IN THE 1950s

621. *Hibs*

622. *Alfie Conn Snr*

623. *4th (four times: 1950-51, 1951-52, 1952-53 and 1954-55)*

624. *8 (in a 8-3 win against Falkirk)*

625. *1,252*

626. *Rangers*

627. *2*

628. *2*

629. *Gordon Marshall*

630. *Gordon Smith*

JOHN COLQUHOUN

631. *1963*

632. *2 (1985-1991 and 1993-1997)*

633. *True: he won 2 caps*

634. *Celtic*

635. *346: 312 (34)*

636. *Rangers*

637. *Striker and winger*

638. *Mark*

639. *Sunderland*

640. *67*

2005/2006

641. George Burley

642. All of them

643. Julien Brellier

644. Livingston, in the CIS Cup

645. Graham Rix

646. 19

647. Rudi Skácel and Paul Hartley

648. Kilmarnock, Aberdeen and Hibernian

649. True (in a 4-2 win over Kilmarnock and in a 1-1 Scottish Cup Final over Gretna)

650. Paul Hartley

ALAN McLAREN

651. James

652. Rangers

653. £2 million

654. 24

655. True

656. Edinburgh

657. 182: 175 (7)

658. 1988

659. Alex MacDonald and Sandy Jardine

660. 7

DAVE MACKAY – 'LEGEND'

661. 1934

662. 1953

663. 1957/58

664. £32,000

665. The Double (League Championship and FA Cup)

666. Brian Clough

667. They won it

668.   *Kuwait*

669.   *22*

670.   *The Heart of Midlothian 'Hall of Fame'*

SCOTT CRABBE

671.   *Striker*

672.   *True*

673.   *Dundee United*

674.   *1968*

675.   *31*

676.   *Livingston*

677.   *False*

678.   *Joe Jordan*

679.   *Falkirk*

680.   *116: 87 (29)*

LEAGUE CUP WINNERS

681.   *4*

682.   *1906*

683.   *3*

684.   *2*

685.   *Motherwell, Partick Thistle, Third Lanark and Kilmarnock*

686.   *1959*

687.   *Johnny Hamilton*

688.   *5-1 v. Partick Thistle in 1958*

689.   *Norrie Davidson*

690.   *Tom 'Tiny' Wharton*

PASQUALE BRUNO

691.   *1962*

692.   *Wigan Athletic*

693.   *Jim Jefferies*

694.   *35: 33 (2)*

695.   Rangers

696.   Juventus

697.   Defender

698.   Celtic

699.   False: he never won a full international cap for Italy

700.   Lecce

HEARTS IN THE 1980s

701.   The First Division

702.   1981/82

703.   A chat show

704.   Alex MacDonald and Sandy Jardine

705.   Alexanders

706.   True

707.   31

708.   Dens Park (Dundee FC)

709.   1987/88

710.   John Robertson

DAVE McPHERSON

711.   2 (1987-1992 and 1994-1999)

712.   1964

713.   Rangers

714.   Alex MacDonald and Sandy Jardine

715.   Celtic

716.   24

717.   Greenock Morton

718.   294: 286 (8)

719.   Defender

720.   27

MISCELLANEOUS - 2

721.   His ear (he was wearing an earring)

722. Colin Cameron

723. Dean Windass

724. Craig Levein and Graeme Hogg

725. 7 (1896, 1906, 1956, 1976, 1986, 1996 and 2006)

726. Westlife

727. Green Street

728. Quizball

729. Scott Wilson

730. Ken Stott

NEIL McCANN

731. 1974

732. 2 (1996-1998 and 2006-2008)

733. Dundee

734. Rangers

735. 3

736. Raith Rovers

737. Stenhousemuir

738. Scottish Cup (during 1997/98)

739. Falkirk

740. Docherty

2006/2007

741. Valdas Ivanauskas

742. Bruno Aguiar, Julien Brellier and Neil McCann

743. Eduard Malofeyev

744. None

745. Steven Pressley, Paul Hartley and Craig Gordon

746. Anatoly Korobochka

747. Hibernian and Dunfermline Athletic

748. Hearts 0, Dundee United 4

749. 10

750. 4th

STEVE FULTON

751. *1970*
752. *15*
753. *Falkirk*
754. *Jim Jefferies*
755. *He blew a kiss to the Hibs fans*
756. *Kilmarnock*
757. *Partick Thistle*
758. *Hibs*
759. *Celtic*
760. *Kilmarnock*

OTHER COMPETITIONS

761. *The Great War (First World War)*
762. *Wolverhampton Wanderers*
763. *George Fleming*
764. *1980/81*
765. *1979/80*
766. *1985 and 1991*
767. *Greenock Morton (won 4-1 in 1985) and Motherwell (won 5-3 in 1991)*
768. *2003 and 2004*
769. *2*
770. *1996*

COLIN CAMERON

771. *Mickey*
772. *Raith Rovers*
773. *Dunfermline*
774. *Stéphane Adam and Andy Kirk*
775. *Wolverhampton Wanderers*
776. *16*
777. *Dundee United*

778.   Jim Jefferies

779.   2

780.   1972

HEARTS AT MURRAYFIELD

781.   Sporting Braga

782.   Andy Webster

783.   Schalke 04 and Ferencváros

784.   Csaba László

785.   NK Široki Brijeg, AEK Athens and Sparta Prague

786.   Emerson

787.   Sparta Prague

788.   Osasuna and Barcelona

789.   Barcelona

790.   Hibernian

STÉPHANE ADAM

791.   Striker

792.   FC Metz

793.   27

794.   Kilmarnock

795.   Kilmarnock

796.   True (in the 52nd minute)

797.   Celtic

798.   4

799.   108: 91 (17)

800.   Lucien

ROALD 'KNIKSEN' JENSEN

801.   1943

802.   Norwegian

803.   'Dribbler'

804.   SK Brann

805. *1964/65*

805. *102*

807. *25*

808. *1976*

809. *31*

810. *SK Brann's 'Brann Stadion'*

THOMAS FLÖGEL

811. **Austrian**

812. **Rangers**

813. **Aberdeen**

814. **5**

815. **Aberdeen**

816. **37**

817. **9**

818. **Jim Jefferies**

819. **Austria Vienna (FK Austria Wien)**

820. **1971**

2007/2008

821. **Sunderland, signing Craig Gordon for £9 million**

822. **Ričardas Beniušis and Audrius Kšanavičius**

823. **Hibernian (they won 1-0)**

824. **Celtic**

825. **Rangers**

826. **6**

827. **Stephen Frail**

828. **Motherwell and Rangers**

829. **True**

830. **8th**

GILLES ROUSSET

831. *1963*

832. *Scottish Cup (in 1998)*

833. *1995*

834. *Stade Rennais*

835. *Geoff Thomas*

836. *2*

837. *False*

838. *Motherwell*

839. *Jim Jefferies*

840. *132*

JIM JEFFERIES

841. *1950*

842. *False: he was born in Musselburgh*

843. *1972*

844. *False: he played for Hearts up until 1981*

845. *Berwick Rangers*

846. *1995*

847. *George Fulston*

848. *Because he put his back out*

849. *3*

850. *1*

ANTTI NIEMI

851. *1999*

852. *Fulham*

853. *False*

854. *Mikko*

855. *Hibernian*

856. *89*

857. *1972*

858. *Finland*

859. *Jim Jefferies*

860. *Southampton*

WHO AM I? - 1

861. Alan Anderson
862. Tommi Grönlund
863. Chris Robertson
864. Gary McSwegan
865. Freddie Glidden
866. Marian Kello
867. Ralph Callachan
868. Kris O'Neil
869. John Millar
870. Jimmy Sandison

STEVEN PRESSLEY

871. Jim Jefferies
872. True
873. Aberdeen
874. Stuttgart
875. 32
876. Falkirk
877. Elvis
878. John
879. Hibernian
880. Celtic

CLASSIC MATCH 1995 – HEARTS 4, RANGERS 2

881. Tommy McLean
882. Colin Miller, Dave McPherson, John Robertson and Kevin Thomas
883. Craig Nelson and Ally Maxwell
884. Brian Laudrup and Gordon Durie
885. False
886. Jim Bett
887. Dave McPherson

888. *True*

889. *Craig Levein, John Robertson and Stephen Frail*

890. *Airdrieonians*

RUDI SKÁCEL

891. *Czech*

892. *Livingston*

893. *True*

894. *Kilmarnock*

895. *True*

896. *16*

897. *1979*

898. *Hibernian*

899. *George Burley*

900. *Marseille*

'22 IN A ROW'

901. *1989-94*

902. *Eamonn Bannon*

903. *13 (drew 9)*

904. *John Robertson and Craig Levein*

905. *11*

906. *Andy Goram*

907. *Wayne Foster*

908. *It was a Scottish Cup match*

909. *Brian Hamilton*

910. *Alex MacDonald, Joe Jordan and Sandy Clark*

PAUL HARTLEY

911. *St Johnstone*

912. *Motherwell*

913. *Kilmarnock*

914. *1976*

915. *Hamilton Academical*

916. *15*

917. *James*

918. *Hibernian*

919. *2007*

920. *Celtic*

2008/2009

921. *Csaba László*

922. *Werner Burger*

923. *David Obua*

924. *Mike Tullberg*

925. *Wolverhampton Wanderers*

926. *Christian Nadé*

927. *Hearts 3, Motherwell 2*

928. *Andrew Driver*

929. *Hristos Karipidis and Rubén Palazuelos*

930. *False: he scored the winner in two of the three games*

ANDRIUS VELIČKA

931. *1979*

932. *Lithuanian*

933. *2006*

934. *St Mirren*

935. *Stranraer*

936. *Glasgow Rangers*

937. *Striker*

938. *Hibernian*

939. *Celtic*

940. *Gretna*

WHO AM I? - 2

941. *Neil MacFarlane*

942. Arthur Mann

943. Maurice Johnston

944. Brian Whittaker

945. Scott Severin

946. Ricardo Fuller

947. Willie Wallace

948. Gary Naysmith

949. José Quitongo

950. Husref Musemić

ANDREW DRIVER

951. David

952. 11

953. Hamilton Academical

954. 1987

955. 5

956. Winger

957. Craig Levein

958. Inverness CT

959. False

960. Michael Stewart and Andrius Velička

WHERE DID THEY COME FROM? - 2

961.	Ramón Pereira	Raith Rovers
962.	Roddy MacDonald	Celtic
963.	David Holt	Queens Park
964.	Samuel Camazzola	Juventude
965.	Jimmy Bone	Hong Kong Rangers
966.	Rab McKinnon	FC Twente
967.	David Kirkwood	Rangers
968.	Stefano Salvatori	Atalanta
969.	Juanjo	Barcelona
970.	Hristos Karipidis	PAOK Salonika

LARYEA KINGSTON

971.   Valdas Ivanauskas

972.   Ghana

973.   10

974.   Richard Kingston

975.   True

976.   St Mirren

977.   5

978.   St Mirren

979.   FC Terek Grozny

980.   Dunfermline Athletic

JOHN ROBERTSON – 'THE HAMMER OF HIBS'

981.   1964

982.   Hibernian

983.   1982

984.   Newcastle United (1988/1989)

985.   1987/88

986.   631

987.   271

988.   27

989.   16

990.   Holding aloft the Scottish Cup

MICHAEL STEWART

991.   1981

992.   Hibernian

993.   Dundee

994.   23

995.   Hearts

996.   Aberdeen

997.   True

998.   Motherwell

999. 3

1000. Manchester United

NOTES:

NOTES:

NOTES:

NOTES:

NOTES:

OTHER BOOKS BY CHRIS COWLIN:

* Celebrities' Favourite Football Teams

* The British TV Sitcom Quiz Book

* The Cricket Quiz Book

* The Gooners Quiz Book

* The Official Aston Villa Quiz Book

* The Official Birmingham City Quiz Book

* The Official Brentford Quiz Book

* The Official Bristol Rovers Quiz Book

* The Official Burnley Quiz Book

* The Official Bury Quiz Book

* The Official Carlisle United Quiz Book

* The Official Carry On Quiz Book

* The Official Chesterfield Football Club Quiz Book

* The Official Colchester United Quiz Book

* The Official Coventry City Quiz Book

* The Official Doncaster Rovers Quiz Book

* The Official Greenock Morton Quiz Book

* The Official Hereford United Quiz Book

* The Official Hull City Quiz Book

* The Official Leicester City Quiz Book

OTHER BOOKS BY CHRIS COWLIN:

* The Official Macclesfield Town Quiz Book

* The Official Norwich City Football Club Quiz

* The Official Notts County Quiz Book

* The Official Peterborough United Quiz Book

* The Official Port Vale Quiz Book

* The Official Rochdale AFC Quiz Book

* The Official Rotherham United Quiz Book

* The Official Shrewsbury Town Quiz Book

* The Official Stockport County Quiz Book

* The Official Watford Football Club Quiz Book

* The Official West Bromwich Albion Quiz Book

* The Official Wolves Quiz Book

* The Official Yeovil Town Quiz Book

* The Reality Television Quiz Book

* The Southend United Quiz Book

* The Sunderland AFC Quiz Book

* The Ultimate Derby County Quiz Book

* The Ultimate Horror Film Quiz Book

* The West Ham United Quiz Book

ALSO BY ANDREW-HENRY BOWIE:

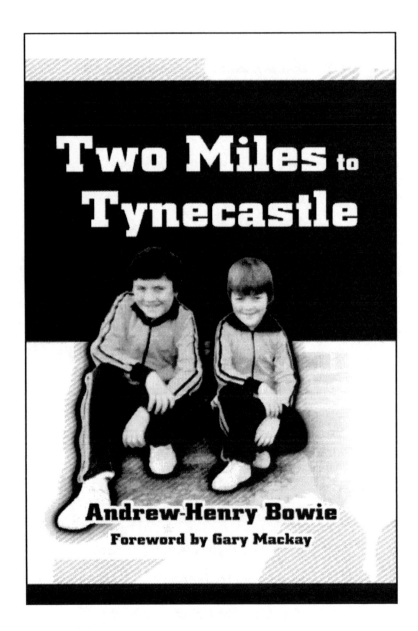

ALSO BY ANDREW-HENRY BOWIE:

Two Miles to Tynecastle

Foreword by Gary Mackay
£9.99 (Hardback)

About the book:
Andrew-Henry Bowie is a passionate Heart of Midlothian Football Club supporter. He doggedly survived a tough childhood and found solace – sort of – in his overwhelming love of football.

The author engages the reader with an energetic and animated account of his years as a Hearts fan and his early years growing up as an Edinburgh 'schemie'. Written with verve and a dry sense of humour Bowie entertains with recollections of a series of calamitous episodes; ironically these seemed to reflect the Hearts' ups and downs!

The book is scattered with familiar references to the 80s and 90s; for anyone growing up during this period, this book will stir poignant memories.

www.apexpublishing.co.uk